A Lad of
Evesham Vale

Also by the same author

The Distant Scene
Under the Parish Lantern
The Secrets of Bredon Hill
The Village of My Childhood
Country Sayings

A Lad of
Evesham Vale

FRED ARCHER

ALAN SUTTON PUBLISHING LIMITED

First published in the United Kingdom in 1972
by Hodder & Stoughton Ltd

First published in this edition in the United Kingdom in 1991
Alan Sutton Publishing Ltd · Phoenix Mill · Far Thrupp · Stroud
Gloucestershire

First published in paperback in 1995

British Library Cataloguing in Publication Data

Archer, Fred *1915*–
A lad of Evesham Vale.
1. Hereford and Worcester (England). Social life, history.
1918–1939
I. Title
914.2447

ISBN 0-7509-0962-5

Typeset in 12/13pt Garamond.
Typesetting and origination by
Alan Sutton Publishing Limited.
Printed in Great Britain by
WBC Limited, Bridgend.

To my good friend and editor
ELSIE HERRON

Author's Note

This book is intended to portray life among the villagers in the Vale of Evesham after the First World War. A life proving the quality of ordinary folk; a mixture of people who to me form a culture that is gone.

The character of Sacco in this book is not based on any one person, living or dead, but draws on various personalities and stories I have encountered in the Vale of Evesham over the years. For although no one person can claim to be any character in my book, these are the sort of folk I have met – who are the backbone of countrylife.

Mine is a privilege which I hope you will share with me.

FRED ARCHER
27 July 1972

Contents

CONTENTS

CHAPTER ONE

Sacco

I first met Sacco in the spring of 1924 when as a small boy I watched a group of men build a dry stone wall in front of the new chapel. The work was being done by volunteers after tea and Sacco was the youngest of them. This seventeen-year-old builder's apprentice cut and laid the stones as well if not better than the older men but he was so different. The older men, cloth-capped and corduroyed, Sacco hatless, his near blond hair brushed straight back, plastered with Jockey Club brilliantine, his round cherub face, pink nose, just slightly askew and those china blue eyes!

It might have been Sunday afternoon the way he was dressed. Smart cut jacket, flannel trousers.

'A rum way to come to work,' Gunner Wood, one of the chapel elders, said to him as he fixed the corner stone by the iron gate. 'Another wench to see after dark, I suppose?'

Sacco straightened his back, strutting past the other men like a cock pheasant and pointing to his motor bike propped against the one damson tree in the chapel yard, answered, 'No doubt I'll be taking one of the choir girls on the pillion for a spin around the hill.'

A five horse-power Norton was a rare possession for a village boy in those days. Martha Blizzard was Sacco's very first conquest. She was maid for Farmer Dunn at the Croft. That evening after the wall builders had knocked off, Sacco kicked up the Norton, revved the engine just to let the older, staid chapel men realize what power he had in it, and Martha mounted the pillion. The long chestnut-coloured hair curled on her shoulders. The old men winked at each other as she hitched up her skirt and cocked her leg over the back wheel.

'He ull break his neck racing round them hairpin bends,'

Joe muttered to Gunner as Sacco's motor bike laid a trail of blue smoke along the Elmley Road.

As the young couple left the village and Sacco's speed read fifty on the clock, Martha's hair left the nape of her neck, the chestnut tresses blew in the spring breeze giving the effect of some modern Boadicea riding her chariot. 'Hang on, Martha!' Sacco shouted above the roar of his engine, 'I'm going to pull all the stops out along the Eckington straight.'

Sacco had slipped a khaki jacket on top of his tweed, a jacket with a belt made of links of leather. Martha leaning forward gripped the bike with her knees, hung on to Sacco with one arm around his waist and one hand holding the leather-linked belt. What a man! What a bike! And those eyes of his, she thought. Oh, if this pillion was meant for me only. Sacco for me only.

By the little stone bridge over Carrants Brook a one-acre meadow was almost wedged between the two hams (water meadows). Here the unlopped withy trees leaned top heavy over the water. The winter's flood had stanked or dammed the brook, forming little islands of brushwood, mud and stones. Sacco and Martha left the motor bike by the field gate. Sacco turned the water tap off the carbide in the headlamp, blowing out the light. Going hand in hand towards the brook the couple disturbed the moorhens sitting on their eggs, nesting on the islands made by the flood. The moorhens' cry made Martha hold Sacco's hand that much tighter. Sacco instinctively laid his khaki coat under the trees and soon they were in each other's arms under the stars, his coat their bed, undisturbed apart from the labouring goods train on the nearby railroad.

'Yield not to temptation,' the Sunday preacher had said. But somehow whether it was Martha's chestnut hair or Sacco's Jockey Club, nature took its course, much in the same way as it had with the neighbouring moorhens earlier in the spring.

'I must be in by ten,' Martha said as she gave Sacco one last hug by the gate. 'Farmer Dunn ull tell our mother, so start up the bike *please*, Sacco.'

SACCO

Sacco first turned the water tap until the carbide produced a gas in the burner of his motor bike lamp, then gave it a light from the Old England's Glory and promised they would be away. The noise of his motor bike broke the evening stillness until near Farmer Dunn's house Sacco shut down the throttle, the bike just purring up to the gate.

'Goodnight, Martha. No doubt we'll meet in the choir on Sunday, then we might go for another spin on the Norton.'

'Nice, Sacco, I'll like that,' Farmer Dunn's maid replied.

In the morning Farmer Dunn shouted up the bare back stairs where the elm boards creak as the feet of farming folk had trodden them for three hundred years. 'Martha, have you seen Harry with the horses yet?'

'No, Sir, he beunt yer yet,' Martha replied rubbing her tired eyes. Dressing in her chill bedroom, she was still dreaming of Sacco. Sacco, she thought, he'll be on the scaffold planks restoring the Abbey. His boss has put him with the stone masons but we will meet at choir practice.

Mr Dunn had put a match to the sticks in the oven grate. As the blue smoke curled up the chimney it was a sign to the workers that his iron kettle swung on the pothook and he would soon be walking breeched and gaitered around the cattle yards. As Martha creaked the elm boards down to the kitchen, standing hair-curlered and sleepy-eyed in front of the singing kettle, Kate Dunn came in from the dairy. She eyed Martha, remarking, 'You were late last night – Sacco, wasn't it?'

'Yes, Ma'am, I was on his motor bike.'

'Now, Martha, everyone likes Sacco but don't let him make a fool of you.'

'No, Ma'am,' she said, 'but he's a nice chap.'

Then in the distance they heard the clip, clop of Harry's haltered team. Harry whistled at the dawn chorus, a starling mocked him, one or two sparks flew from the shoes of Violet the broodmare as she stumbled gingerly over the Clee Hill stones down the lane. His dog Rough followed him, working the hedges for rabbits, a morning scramble through the tracks in the briar as Harry led the team. George Blizzard, ash plant in hand, swayed morning-dazed up the lane. George, who had not helped build the chapel wall but had spent the evening before at the Dragon, said, 'His yud punished him,' as he drove the cows. 'Punished for abuse, I suppose,' he thought. 'Damn your pelts, you occud lot of cow bags,' he shouted, then realized Ada had calved in the meadow and stayed behind. 'Coop, coop, coop, come on,' he shouted back at her, but she bawled for her calf. In the stalls George's monotonous tit lugging filled buckets of milk. *Chee, chaw, chee, chaw,* the milk sang in George's pail as George's cap, back to front and red with cow hair, was pushed by his head into the right flank of each cow in her turn. *Moo, moo* resounded from the meadow as Ada licked her calf, now standing as if on four straight stilts, afraid to move until at last it found Ada's udder and sucked, wagging its tail.

'We wants the float, Gaffer,' George told Farmer Dunn who stood by the churns with hands in breech pockets up to his elbows.

'Another calf, George, then?' Farmer Dunn said. 'Is it a heifer?'

'Don't know ett, Gaffer, but we shall have to get them both in. If I knows Ada she ull have a bag like a bushel measure.'

'Oh, yes,' Mr Dunn replied, as George tackled the next milking cow, stool in one hand, bucket in the other. 'She's a five-gallon cow.'

George under his breath whispered, 'The kicking sod, I bin dreading her calving down.' Then Harry brought the float round with the pony that took the milk to the station and he and George lifted the calf into the float, Ada following behind.

''Tis a heifer calf,' George said, lifting its tail. 'It is to be hoped her won't kick like her mother in three years' time.'

In the stall Ada mooed for her calf in the nearby pen while George muttered, 'You blasted beast, kip still, ull ya, kicking at me. It unt the fust time you have bin confined.' George didn't sit on the stool to milk Ada but stood milking the cherry curds one-handed into the pail. The yellow, poor man's cream would make a pudding for George and his wife, providing Ada didn't kick the bucket over. 'There, the calf can have the rest,' George said, as he left mother and daughter together in a loose box.

Martha came into the cowshed as Harry and George loaded the churns of milk in the float for the railway station.

'What's it like on Sacco's Norton?' they both said, 'I suppose you knows you to be the fust wench as he's been out with according to all accounts?'

Martha blushed, thinking to herself that he didn't do so bad. He must have an inbred way with women. Still, she thought, the preacher said, 'To everything there is a season and a time to every purpose under heaven. A time to love, a time to hate.'

Sacco worked with the masons on the Abbey church at Tewkesbury where the Norman craftsmen had spent a lifetime seven hundred and fifty years ago building the Severnside shrine. Only the best men were fit to renew such a masterpiece where time and weather had taken its toll. Sacco cut stone as Kate Dunn cut butter.

At chapel choir practice, Joe's wife Emma pedalled the harmonium while Mercy, the big blowsy wife of Gunner, conducted. Young Sacco was developing into a useful tenor. Martha sang with the sopranos in the anthem. Gunner and Frank, together at work on their smallholding by the brook, both sang bass at the chapel. After practice, as the shadows lengthened and the dew and mist enveloped the Stone Bridge ground on the bank of Carrants Brook, Sacco was eager. Eager to take Martha under the withies. 'We'll skip the run round the hill tonight,' he said, and the two choristers rode the Norton to the Brook meadows.

'Mrs Dunn says I got to be careful with you, Sacco,' Martha said as they dismounted. 'You got a passionate look in your eyes.'

Sunday service at chapel, where the preacher spoke of 'The Better Land' and 'Man cannot live on bread alone', started Sacco's mind working. He thumbed his bible where he read, 'It is not good for man to live alone,' and thought as his blue eyes scanned the choir girls, 'I'll not tie myself to Martha, not even to the chapel girls. I saw Amy today as she walked down the village. There is something very special about Amy.' Dreaming through the sermon and awakened suddenly to Gunner's shout of Hallelujah, he filed out with the others shaking hands with the preacher, and rode home alone on the Norton. Frank nodded to Gunner whispering, 'I udn't like to see young Martha get into trouble. It do happen to chapel folk, 'tis nature and nature takes a lot of curbing when you be young and gallus.' The preacher, a brother of Gunner, a platelayer on the Midland Railway, walked clutching the Book down the village to Gunner's house where his sister-in-law, Mercy, had supper laid. Then home to his family and bed. He hung his Sunday black suit on the bedside chair, his trousers lay like two drain pipes, and he lay in bed on the tick full of breast feathers from the poultry of Christmases past, snoring peacefully, dreaming of the Golden Gates as his Albert watch ticked away the night hours in his waistcoat pocket. The alarm clock, set for six o'clock, stood on the marble stand by the jug and basin. He must be up early; a platelayer, even on our branch line, must walk the length of the line using a sledge-hammer to drive all displaced wooden wedges into their chairs which grip the four-foot way.

Every spring morning, Joe, Gunner, Mercy and Emma, Joe's wife, pulled the onions, cut the gillies for the market lorry. Gunner, in the smallholders' hovel, tied the bunched onions into dozens with withy twigs, and washed them in Carrants Brook. The women tied the gillies with raffia, tied the onions with soft string. With flat-bottomed wheelbarrows the men wheeled the produce of Carrants field to the lane where Harry's lorry took it to Cheltenham. (Harry was the local carrier.) 'A good word your brother gave last night at chapel,' Joe said. 'I hope it fell on good ground. I be mortal worried about Sacco, he don't seem to be quite on the straight and narra way!'

''Tis in the family,' Gunner replied, 'anything with a skirt on, they be after it.' Sacco, unaware of the interest of the chapel elders, cut and laid stones in the Abbey's restoration. Whistling, singing, winking at the town girls from his scaffold, then scorching home on his Norton past the thatched cottage where Martha's cousin Alice lived with her father George Blizzard. As the dust settled on the hedges from Sacco's motor bike, dust caused by a full throttle for the Blizzards' benefit, Dunn's cowman stood at the door exclaiming to his neighbour Harry. 'That bwoy ull be the death a me rattling past yer, or he ull break his blasted neck.'

CHAPTER TWO

Flora Lights

Harbour Lights, ex-naval man, spent his last years at a hillside cot known as Coney Burrows. Harbour had suffered badly in the navy during the first war. He contracted pneumonia on service in the North Sea and developing T.B. was discharged with one lung. Harbour got his name through sending telegrams signed, 'Harbour' to Flora, his wife, every possible time when he landed. This went back to before the war when he courted Flora, the daughter of the quarryman on the hill.

There was little hope for Harbour when I knew him. He ambled the village on the sick list, a victim of war. Tall, thin, he had fathered a big family – a family of handsome boys and pretty girls. While Harbour withered away, Flora was very game, firmly believing that there is nothing more wonderful than the way of a man with a woman. While Harbour coughed his way to the next world in the bedroom of Coney Burrows, Flora made love with horse-trainers, broken-down farmers and such in the kitchen.

'It's like that with some women,' Gunner told them at chapel. 'Like the Bore as comes up the Severn in the spring, thur's no stopping it.'

Harbour died when I was but a small boy. They buried him under the churchyard wall, a Union Jack covered his coffin as men with medals and black cloth caps wheeled the bier down the village street. I'd heard of widow's weeds and Flora Lights draped herself in these and everyone was sorry for her and her children. When I say 'everyone', not quite everyone.

'No better than she should be,' the upright, self-righteous, never-did-any-wrong women of the Mothers' Union said. A few, the ignorant, or maybe the spiteful, stayed away from the Union because Flora went.

As her family grew up and left school, she walked up and down the road with her two youngest – Amy and Lil – and what a handsome pair they were. Flora, to the disgust of the working women, went on the Parish, drawing relief. Harbour's navy pension was meagre, money went through Flora's hands like water. She bought expensive clothes to follow the widow's weeds. Cars came from the towns and villages in the Vale; Flora was a hostess to the frustrated men of Evesham Vale. Another blow struck when her eldest son died. Again, most humane, the villagers were sad for Flora.

'I can't forget the way I was brought up,' she told us in the farmhouse. 'My Father had a groom when he ran the quarry. My Mother had a cook and two housemaids.' Flora told her tale of woe in our kitchen by the oven grate as the oil lamp reflected its light on the shining knobs of the oven. Pathetic she looked but somehow dignified, her slightly greying hair in a bun and a ribbon of velvet around her neck. Flora struggled her way through life, never backward in asking assistance. With the cast-off clothes of Lady Gertrude's family, she kept her family smarter than average. An expert letter writer, she usually added: P.S. Lil's size in shoes is size three – or something to that effect.

The ganger on the Midland branch line retired. Gunner's preacher brother refused the extra few shillings a week, remaining a platelayer rather than have the responsibility of 'the length', so Ganger Firth arrived in the village from the Forest of Dean. He spoke a strange tongue with his h'ms and his ums, but he wanted lodgings. Flora put him up at Coney Burrows. Flora could cook, she could wash and her cot on the hill was clean. A board and lodging allowance from the ganger would help her enormously, she thought, little knowing that the Relieving Officer would want an amended account of her income. Still, Flora was better off with a man about the house. His tattooed arms like legs of mutton, his broad back, railway pattern sleeve waistcoat, became a familiar sight as he carried hundred-weight bags of coal up the hill from the village. Dark, swarthy, with a sort of Ronald Colman moustache, he

soon settled in with Flora at the Burrows. The sleeping
arrangements up on the hill were anybody's guess and nobody's
business.

Flora Lights, always short of rent money, grocery money, was
on one occasion left without enough to pay her railway fare to
Evesham. When she asked Ganger Firth as he came in one
dinner time for a few shillings to spend and enough to pay her
fare on the two-twenty to town, the man of the Forest of Dean
went down the garden of Coney Burrows, between the damson
trees and through the gate into Sloe Down. Here in a field full of
milking cows and in-calf heifers, Farmer Dunn kept a donkey.
It was always supposed that by keeping a donkey among the
milkers they would never 'slip a calf' – the term used by local
stockmen for an abortion. Ganger grabbed the donkey and led
him up the garden of Coney Burrows into the scrubbed kitchen
where the red tiles gleamed on the floor of the Lights' house.

'Cock yer leg over that, Flora. That ull take you to Evesham –
all you wants is a bit of patience,' and with a fresh pulled garden
carrot, Ganger fed the donkey. Flora saw the funny side as the
railwayman and his stubborn animal got stuck in the house, the
donkey refusing to budge. More carrots from the garden enticed
the donkey back to Sloe Down.

As Joe and Gunner talked this over on the smallholding, Joe
said very seriously, 'If ever Neddy had have cocked his derum in
the kitchen, lors what a mess.'

Harbour Lights' second daughter, Amy, left the sleep of the
village to draw pints for the working men at the Railway Hotel,
pints of beer where the occasional hop floated on the tankard,
short drinks for the market-going farmers and stout for the town
women. Lil left school and went into service at the house of an
elderly couple. The husband had retired from Government
service in New Zealand. Fourteen-year-old Lil had not yet the
appeal of Amy, but her rosy cheeks, her upright walk gave her a
distinctive air – no doubt inherited from Flora who one must
not forget was of gentle stock – 'Father had a groom, Mother
had a houseful of servants.'

Lil's few shillings a week at service gave her little scope for the Scala at Evesham and punting on the river on Sunday. Monday morning she rose early at Coney Burrows, breakfasting with Ganger Firth and Flora. Flora's neckband of velvet seemed to signify gentility but Flora was an outcast with some. '"Scarlet" they calls our Mother,' Lil said. 'But I don't care.' So Lil walked upright and brazen down the village to the chapel. Up the steps, past the wall Sacco helped to build; she unlocked the vestry door where the bucket, the broom and brush waited her Monday morning cleaning. As she had passed the cottage women, windows were opened and slammed, curtains were drawn. 'You can talk,' she thought. 'Talk about our Mother and Amy at the Railway Hotel. What about Dad as died soon after the war?' The windows slammed in the cottage bedrooms, the cottage kitchens, by the church-married-never-done-any-wrong wives of the parish. Humming a hymn, Lil scrubbed the steps. She thought of Frank and Gunner on their smallholding. 'Helped our Mum they did with vegetables when we were at school.' She dusted the table where last night the Lord's Supper was observed by Gunner's brother and the men who called each other brother. 'What a mess they made last night. Oh, yers a sixpence under the pulpit but I'll put it in the mission box. That's it for another week and another shilling earned by me. Our Mother's lodger,' she thought, 'what do the tattooes say on his arms? There are anchors, hearts and "I Love You". His bin in the navy like our Dad was. Our Mother likes him. He sleeps with her like our Dad did. She bin banned from the Mothers' Union but the chapel still has a place for her. Our Mother says hers more at home on the pitchpine benches than the old oak pews down at the Revd Vernon's church. Pews that go over the grave stones of the three-hundred-years-dead. Must smell in there, not like when I've carbolicked the chapel. Still it suits them as likes it that way.'

At the Railway Hotel in town Amy Lights stood behind the bar – a rural Venus. At eighteen she had developed into perhaps the finest looking girl the village had given birth to. When she walked to the station for her job in the town every morning except Sunday, carters stopped their horses on the roadside headland, lads on bikes twisted their necks, gentlemen in cars took their eyes off the road to see this. Some competitor in what could have been a parade of the mannequins. Young wives watched their husbands in the evenings as she homed on the seven o'clock train. Amy Lights took the village by storm. Amy Lights took some village menfolk to the Railway Hotel on Saturday nights. As she grew up and rode in the cars of the Evesham merchants to the hills, the riverside, presents were lavished on her – fur coats, glittering handbags – and she became the best dressed of all the females of the hill villages.

Sacco from the chapel choir saw her walk past on Sundays. Amy waited for Flora to pass through the wicket garden gate to chapel. Flora passed, Lil passed, Sacco crept to Coney Burrows.

'It's nice on the hill tonight, Amy. Quiet now half the village are at chapel, half at church. Care for a stroll?'

'I'll be out in a tick. Our Mother's left me the washing up.'

But soon Sacco had his heart's desire – to escort Amy up through the flowering grasses and the seeding gorse where on this hot summer's night the pods crackled like horse whips after the day's sunshine.

Since his evenings with Martha, Sacco had been out with most of the village girls. He had spent evenings on Tewkesbury Ham by the river as the sun sank over the Malverns with stonemasons' daughters from the Abbey.

The sight of Amy took Sacco's breath for a moment until she said, 'Why aren't you at chapel? Aren't you in the choir?'

'As a matter of fact,' said Sacco, 'I had the inclination tonight to take an evening stroll with the most beautiful female creature who ever walked Bredon Hill.'

'I've heard all that blarney in the bar.' Amy tossed her head, looking Sacco straight into his china blue eyes.

The rabbits ran in front of the couple to their warrens further up the slope, their white tails popping up and down like a line of powder puffs, then underground the unmistakable thump of older ones to the young to get under the hill where the holes went deep under the elder bushes, and the heaps of yellow fresh moved earth lay trodden and manured at the mouth.

'You seldom come into the Railway,' Amy said, as if disappointed. 'When I don't get a lift, I come back on the late train on Saturdays. Some nights I don't come home. People are good to me since Dad died.'

'Good to you,' Sacco thought. 'Not much of an effort needed to be good to you,' he said.

'Our Mother's back from chapel at ten past seven,' Amy butted in. So among the gorse and on a bed of wire grass the young couple lay. Overtures, they call this in music.

'I'm learning the organ, Amy,' Sacco said, as Amy threw her arms around the clean shaven youth with a wicked look in his eye. For some minutes Sacco lay with his head between the softest bosoms he had seen. Bosoms like the knolls in the hillside field.

'Sacco,' she said, 'Martha's got nothin like me, has she?' And before the preacher at chapel announced the last hymn, Sacco and Amy heard the music of love. They made love among the summer flowers until they saw Flora Lights walking along to Coney Burrows. Lil had gone off with the village boys, Sacco stalked as if he was after one of the deer from the park, through the elder bushes to the village. Amy brushed her crêpe de chine dress, combed her hair, walked through the back wicket gate through the garden to the house. Flora climbed the hill clutching her Moody and Sankey hymn book and in the kitchen prepared Ganger Firth's supper – Ganger Firth preferring the Dragon Inn for worship.

'Pity it isn't Sunday every day and the gorse pods pop after a summer sun,' Sacco thought, as he mounted his saddle on the long petrol-tanked Norton. A tank, he thought that when full would take him and Amy into the mountains of Wales. He squeezed the rubber bulb of the horn, fixed as it was to the handlebars – handlebars wide apart like the antlers of a deer. *Parp, parp* went the horn outside Blizzards' cottage. By the time George had opened his front door, all that was left of Sacco or the Norton was the stench of petrol exhaust and the distant purr of a five-horse-power engine.

'Damn it, as the church folk ud say, if Sacco won't break his neck along the Beckford Way,' George said to Mrs Blizzard, his wife. 'Our Alice I be must afraid got a liking for Sacco. Martha doesn't go out uv him no more – he's fast like his motor bike.'

The master man at Coney Burrows, Ganger Firth, came down to the Dragon more and more often; the wine of the west was getting the better of the man of the forest. True, he walked his length on time on the Midland branch but his payments to Flora were irregular. Flora, hungry for fine clothes as well as a man, left Coney Burrows for a fortnight. Amy lived in at the Railway, Lil stayed at Mercy's.

Every night at the Dragon, Ganger Firth quaffed quarts of local cider until the wasps followed the ferment of his breath up the hill to Coney Burrows. A card, delivered by postwoman Cissy Treadwell, read that Flora would return on the Saturday night on the eight-twenty from Cheltenham. That Saturday afternoon, Ganger climbed the stepladder to the attic, found up there a grand Union Jack – a bit moth-eaten since the peace celebrations of 1919 but still intact with its pole. Pinning the pole in the sash bedroom window, he lowered the flag so that it wafted in the breeze over Coney Burrows. 'It yunt Empire Day,' Jos said to Gunner as he passed to Carrants Field. 'No, nor it unt the King's birthday, I wonder what the man off the Midland Railroad is celebrating.'

Gunner said, 'Well, he a bin celebrating at the Dragon for a fortnight, a-blueing his wages while Flora bin away and Cissy told Mercy today that Flora comes whome tonight on the last train. Cissy couldn't help but read the postcard, 'twas from Weston. Donkeys on the front to remind Ganger of Dunn's donkey.' Ganger Firth had his final fling at the Dragon that Saturday night. Some said he was paralytic, George Blizzard said he was prostitute until the landlord's wife corrected him and said surely he meant prostrate.

Flora walked the road from the station, picked up Lil at Mercy's on the way and half expected Ganger to meet her to carry her case. Ganger had still not yet slaked his thirst. Coney Burrows, locked back and front, gave no access to Flora. Waiting at the front door, seeing the floating from the Union Jacked bedroom, she sent Lil back to Gunner and Mercy's house for help. Gunner, like most village folk in the late Twenties, kept a ladder under the thatched eaves of his cottage, hanging on two wooden pegs; a ladder to pick his garden plums or in case of fire to climb the roof. He carried the ladder to Coney Burrows, climbed to the flag-bedecked window and pushed open the sash. 'Where dost want this emblem?' he shouted to Flora, 'or is it special?' 'Throw it down on the garden and climb into the bedroom,' she answered. In the bedroom Gunner saw quart bottles of cider. He shouted to Flora, 'Your man a got cider under the bed instead of the jerry.'

Gunner unfurled the flag almost reverently, folded it and placed it by Firth's bed. Downstairs he opened the door and let Flora in. Flora, tired with her cases, asked Gunner to fetch a bucket of water from the standpipe. In Coney Burrows the chapel market gardener felt like a trapped bird as he sat in the kitchen with a woman who continually needed a man. The kettle boiled on the oil stove and Flora made the tea. As they sipped and quenched their thirst the couple speculated on why Ganger had hoisted the flag and locked the door.

Turning out time at the Dragon and cider-sodden Ganger Firth was incapable of the quarter-of-a-mile walk to Coney Burrows.

'Flora Lights ull murder tha when you gets whome,' Harry Blizzard said.

'Now you chaps,' said Fred Cooper, 'the Ganger wants some help tonight, surely two of you can help him up the road.'

Harry and George Blizzard armed him through the five-barred gate of the Dragon and half carried the Ganger to the home of his landlady. At the doorway the Ganger was almost asleep on the Blizzards' arms. They sat him against the door, hammered on the knocker and ran to the gate waiting. Waiting for Flora Lights, to hear her tongue wagging, to see what reception the Ganger would have.

As she opened the door sharply, Firth's body, which up till then was in a sitting position, rolled at her feet into the little entrance hall of Coney Burrows. She kicked it like a boy kicking a football. She called him every wicked word she could lay her tongue to. The Blizzards, not anxious to get involved with the home life of Mrs Lights and Mr Firth, went soberly to their cottages up the lane, where even on the darkest nights the black and white showed up under the thatch and the yellow glow of the paraffin lamps gleamed through the curtains.

CHAPTER THREE

Sacco Leaves the Abbey

In his early twenties Sacco decided that the long restoration job on the Abbey had become tedious. Every morning, wet or fine, he mounted the Norton, goggled, helmeted, leather-coated, gauntleted, khaki motor cycle legginged.

'He roars through the parish "like an hexpress train",' Joe told Gunner as they hoed the asparagus beds.

'Why don't he allow himself a feow more minutes,' Gunner replied, 'a go steady to Tewkesbury.'

Sacco started on his own, contracting for stone wall work, tiling the Cotswold houses. Like most tradesmen of that day, he took the occasional day off.

Amy Lights grew into an indescribable beauty. She lived in part of the time at the Evesham hotel where she worked, then she moved to one of the finest old inns in the town – an old coaching inn. Here, after the cloth was placed over the handles of her beer engine at closing time and the washing up was done, she occupied a bedroom on the second floor. Sacco stayed long after closing time but he could not leave this daughter of Harbour Lights.

He had been working in the town on the stonework of one of the churches. His ladder lay under the laurel hedge by the churchyard wall. At midnight he carried the ladder to the inn and hoisted it to Amy's window. Amy knew beforehand and left the sash wide open for Sacco's entry. 'Flora had a man, so why shouldn't I?' thought Amy. So both enjoyed the home comforts until morning when a passing policeman inquired about the ladder.

Amy shoved Sacco in the wardrobe where he stayed all day while Amy went on with her work at the bar. When darkness fell once more, Sacco slipped down his ladder, carried it back to the churchyard and turned the Norton homewards, unsuspected, undetected. In the late Twenties illicit sex was looked upon by Gunner, the chapel market gardeners and Millie Bostock, who ran the Mothers' Union, as a kind of passport to Hell. 'Fornication' Mercy called it. The quite recent slaughter (on the Somme), of men in their prime, the dire poverty of the dole, the bread lines, were mere bagatelle in the eyes of some of the Holy Ones.

Sacco told me that if the good Lord had known of any blessing more pleasurable which he could bestow on the human race, he had so far kept it to himself. The masons at the Abbey lost a good man when Sacco went freelance. He was in demand from now on restoring the houses of character, houses of the professional classes and the retired Birmingham business men.

Teddy Pride, known in the village as Monkey Brand, red bearded with striking resemblance to the face on the polish tin, lived in a three-storey Georgian house with an apple orchard. It is difficult to imagine what Mrs Pride saw in Monkey Brand, but they stood before the holy table at the village church agreeing to live together 'for better, for worse, till death us do part' in the late afternoon of their lives. Teddy, a retired farmer, took on the responsibilities of married life. He engaged Sacco to rebuild the stone gateposts, replace cracked door and window lintels and generally improve the house in the orchard.

'I wish you all the best in your married life, Mr Pride,' Sacco told him one day as he trowelled the capping stone on his gatepost. 'An extremely wise man you are,' Sacco added, 'when the age for the procreation of children has past.'

'Procreation,' Teddy grinned, as he always grinned. 'That's a big word for a young single chap like you.'

Sacco whispered to Teddy out of Mrs Pride's earshot, 'Alice Blizzard has got something under her petticoat. In a way of speaking she is expecting a happy event. It was my foot that slipped, I've colted her.'

'Sacco,' Monkey Brand exclaimed, 'you will marry her no doubt.'

'That's a difficult decision to make. You see Amy Lights is more my kidney.'

As the house in the orchard became more of a home fit for the Prides, Sacco saw the comings and goings of married bliss. He saw Monkey Brand blue-aproned, red-bearded, kneel before the altar of Mrs Pride's oven grate. He saw through the window as he fixed the stone over the porch with the words Hill View cut in the Cotswold slab. Teddy knelt there brushing black lead on the oven door in the kitchen, black lead on the hob until the whole thing shone as if grinning back at the grinning bridegroom of a month.

Mrs Pride, upright, corsetted, big bosomed, did her daily round of inspection. She dwarfed Teddy. She had been used to servants at her father's farmhouse, housemaids to cook and a gardener groom who spent a lot of his time with the pony harnessed to the governess cart waiting. Waiting for orders from Mrs Pride's mother to take her and her daughter to town, sitting on the navy-blue cushions with only the tinkle of the silver mounted harness to be heard in the country lanes of her youth. Now it was different. Monkey Brand, besides being bedmate to his wife, was being trained in the domestic side of the house. 'Quick now, Teddy,' she says, 'we are due at church at ten. Get the firewood, get the coal, peel the potatoes, prepare the greens, pick some gooseberries.' The subdued little man, who had never dreamed of sleeping in a double bed until nearly sixty years of age had passed, submitted, just adding meekly, 'What next? What next?'

Mrs Pride dusts the parlour, brushes the stairs with the hand brush until all the choking dust leaves the carpet, then they both get ready for church on a Saint's Day. Mrs Pride dresses again in her Sunday, navy, shot-silk, trimmed with lace dress. Her hat and veil have the last adjustment in the hall mirror. She dare not smile in case her powdered, pasted face cracks like frosted cement. Teddy, black-suited, black-booted, black-bowlered, gold-watch-chained, locks the front door, pockets the key, winks at Sacco as he, terrier-like, follows the sedate piece of untouchable femininity down the street. Mrs Pride's chin cocks up so high that she would be quite unaware of any loose stone until she tripped on it. Teddy's eyes twinkled as he walked behind her, wondering all the time if one day he dare go foremost to church.

Sacco thought, 'That's marriage, that won't be for me and Alice. Oh no!' After Sacco's night at the Evesham hotel with Amy Lights, Amy used to catch the last train home on Saturdays to our village station. The driver, the guard, the porter on that five-mile length of Midland Railway knew Amy, they knew Sacco. Somehow as the late train left Evesham station and Amy Lights and the mason chose an empty compartment for their journey to the village, there was a conspiracy between the staff. They all assumed, in fact they all knew, exactly what went on in the red and black plush seats of the compartment. Sacco told the guard to tell the engine driver 'to take his time to our station'.

Five minutes between stations was the average time, but from the last stop before our village it usually took a little longer – there was the incline. A packet of ten Woodbines was Sacco's present for what he described as 'a touch' between the last two stations. The preliminaries were doubtless gone through soon after the little tank engine blew her steam over the river bridge outside Evesham station, the final intimacy as the train left the last halt before the village. A signal from the guard to the driver and the three coaches rocked and rolled Sacco and Amy on the Midland plush those last three miles until they handed in their pasteboard tickets at our village. It was a sort of competition between drivers those Saturday nights – how quickly they could get those coaches over the last three miles of iron road while Amy and Sacco would have liked it to have been thirty miles nonstop.

Amy knew about Alice Blizzard but didn't care, knowing full well that after Sacco had been parsonned, he would still let the Midland engine drivers on our branch line have their fun and Amy would not go un-neglected when her Mother was at chapel on Sunday nights. There was still the gorse and the larks on the hill, the hour of bliss, the thumping of Sacco's heart, the thumping of the rabbits going to ground above Coney Burrows.

With Alice Blizzard 'in the family way', Sacco steered a course not uncommon with men in the building trade. He observed Mondays as 'A Day for the King', a day to get over his weekends. Weekends he spent with Amy at Coney Burrows, with Ganger at the Dragon. Sacco still found time to spend an hour at chapel on Sundays when Amy was working.

Gunner and Mercy were upset but not surprised at Alice's condition. 'Them as plays with fire ull burn thur fingers in time,' Gunner said. 'Poor wench,' Mercy added. 'I see her av ad to let her stays out. Folks talks about girls as walks big-bellied up the village street. Ent it time Sacco married her respectable like?'

At the Dragon George Blizzard was always bought a pint by Sacco but he, Alice's father, told Sacco to be a man and marry his daughter 'or else thur ull be hell to pay when urs confined.'

Sacco, a nineter at darts, doubles and trebles for a pastime. When he got the feathers in the outer circle on top of Fred Cooper's board and the company shouted 'Up in Annie's Room', Sacco thought what a fool he had been to get Alice in pod.

On a bright Saturday morning, with little ceremony, Sacco promised Alice in front of the chapel pulpit 'to live with her till death us do part', as simple as that. Farmer Dunn rented a little Cotswold cottage on the hill to Sacco and Alice. 'Damn glad I be that our Alice won't have a bastard kid,' George Blizzard said, 'although young Sacco is a torrel — earning money and letting it through his hands like water.' Mercy and

Emma prayed at chapel for the couple, knowing that this marriage was what Ganger from the Forest called 'a shot-gun job'. Revd Vernon at the church prayed that the blessing of the Almighty might be with them. You see there was something about Sacco that everyone liked. Young girls, not yet bespoke, looked at him with eyes like saucers. The young wives watched him with a kind of envy, comparing him with their men who lacked his spirit. Young married men kept an eye on where his Norton motor bike was propped in case he seduced their wives. The village had never had anyone like Sacco live there before.

CHAPTER FOUR

The Parson, Cyril and Stodge

Revd Vernon rode his tricycle religiously between our two parishes. A great believer in cocoa, when visiting the sick he usually waited for the coupons inside the tins – he collected them. A Low Churchman was Vernon. He had no option. Cyril Pumfrey, his brother-in-law, and organist Millie Bostock neither bowed nor scraped in front of the eagle on the pulpit or the holy table.

Parson Vernon excelled at funerals. He had a voice full of comfort to rich and poor alike. He had a good helper in Cyril, the churchwarden. Arriving from the next parish, mopping his brow, the parson left his tricycle in Millie's garden. Jasper Hill, hurdle-maker, had left his bench and passed the bell all morning. Stodge the roadman saw the whole event as he swung his stockaxe at the roadside verge, smoke billowing from his clay pipe, his nose-warmer. Stodge was one of the ageless countrymen in the village who in his youth drove steam engines; now he worked for the Council. Cyril Pumfrey left his bachelor lodging at the top end, tied his fox terrier, Rex, to the hogshead water butt, lit his pipe, always a silver-banded pipe, and with his silver-banded walking stick walked as a church-warden should sedately down towards the church. *Yap, yap*, Rex barked. Cyril barked back, 'Lie down, you can't come today.'

As Stodge straightened his back and stood his full five feet two in his corduroys, yorked trousers, sleeve waistcoated, he laid down his stockaxe and shovelled the usual morning muck from Harry's horse team and George's cows outside Farmer Dunn's.

'Nice marning,' Cyril greeted him.

'Oi, it was fust thing, that is if thee wast up to see it.'

Cyril pushed a shilling into Stodge's hand. They had an understanding about the tidying up of the village street. As Cyril strode down towards the funeral, Stodge listened to Cyril's footsteps, heard his throat clearing, sniffing, saw the pepper-and-salt suited churchwarden with ox-blood-coloured boots disappear down the hill with his usual shoulder shrugging. What a picture Stodge made with his wheelbarrow, red flag, his tools, his coat hanging on the hawthorn. Monkey Brand Pride walked alone past the barrow. Stodge's comments about Cyril, despite the shilling, were caustic. 'See our warden just go by sniffing and keckling. He had his tonsils burnt out the t'other wick in Brummigum but he still keckles smartish. I'll tell thee what it is, Master Pride, these yer townees beunt the same as thee and me. They foreigners from up North Country be foryud. The cheek of Old Nick they got!'

Teddy Pride grinned, said nothing. Despite the fact it was a funeral he was free, free from the constant orders of the Lady of Hill View.

Stodge saw nothing but just heard Jasper Hill's bell. It was bait time, so he who had breakfasted at six, worked since seven, slumped, legs akimbo, in his wheelbarrow to eat his thumb piece of bread and fat bacon, to swig his cider. He heard the farmer's nags go by, loads of hay, of mangolds, pulled by Dunn's horses driven by the farm boys. They passed unnoticed by Stodge. Then down the hill he heard the slow march of death as four men pulled the flower-covered bier where the body of an old villager lay encased in oak. Stodge got down from his barrow, pushed it into the grass, then taking off his battered trilby with the grease-stained hat band, stood upright and bald, solemn as a judge, as the little procession passed. Gunner and Joe walked past from their smallholding, cap in hand and stood with Stodge as the bier passed.

'Can't fancy any more fettle and drink,' Stodge says. 'I used to go to school along uv that mon in the box.'

Gunner, always ready to put a word in about eternity says, 'Stodge, it's got to come to us all sooner or later. The most important thing is to have your house in order.'

'Now, Gunner,' Stodge replies, 'I got no time for chapel hand-shaking or church psalm-singing, but I specks I be as good a mon as thee bist.'

'It unt that,' Joe added, 'it's faith in the Almighty you want, Stodge.'

Down at the fifteenth-century cross where men worshipped God perhaps before the church was built, Cyril Pumfrey is impatient for the little funeral party to arrive. Millie Bostock chats with the robed vicar, stands with her wreath, then turning to Cyril says, 'Are you going to blow my organ or shall I have to pedal?'

'I might,' Cyril replies, knocking his pipe out on the bottom step of the cross.

'Might,' answers Millie, 'you would let me pedal?'

'Well, lend me your hard broom after the funeral so that I can sweep the path.'

'Alright, Cyril, you townee foreigner, I've got more bones in the churchyard than you have.'

'Women!' Cyril thinks, 'Bah,' and they both enter the church.

By now Jasper is passing the bell more often as the coffin on the bier enters the gates. George Blizzard driving a cow and calf of Dunn's up the road, notices that one of the pancake black-capped bearers of the coffin is Sacco. 'Funny man, Sacco,' he thought, 'he sat up nights along uv the mon they be burying, night after night comforting him, then to work in the day. Alice hasn't got far to go now. They seems happy enough up in Dunn's cottage, a youngster in the house might steady him.'

In the church, waiting for the mourners, sat Flora Lights, Miss Badger, Miss Curtis. 'I beunt one to criticize,' Stodge told Pumfrey after the funeral, 'but they likes the look of the Reverend and they likes the look of you – it's a mon they wants. I udn't wish Millie on yar but Miss Curtis or Miss

Badger ud do ya good. Dost ever read the Bible, Master Pumfrey, 'cos it says in thur it unt good for man to live alone!'

Cyril, changing the subject, said, 'I'd like you to tidy up round the village green, Stodge, before Sunday. I see someone has been over it with a car.'

'Oi, and who do you think it was?' Stodge said, as he stood with one foot on the barrow and holding his clay pipe. 'The man as made them tyre ruts was the Reverend from the next parish.'

'I'll see him,' Cyril replied. 'What's sauce for the gander is sauce for the goose,' and offering Stodge his tobacco pouch he invited him to fill his clay again. 'But just patch it up with a bit of turf, Stodge, it does look bad by the church gates.'

Millie Bostock, a virgin who ran the Mothers' Union, depended on Cyril and Monkey Brand to fetch and carry for her. The high teas she gave in the reading room were fabulous affairs: ham off the bone, homemade cakes, but the tea was from the village urn. The water boiled in the copper. On afternoons when the hats and costumes were carried on the frames of the upholders of the sanctity of marriage down the village street to the reading room, Cyril in shirt sleeves carried buckets of water from the church standpipe to the tea. Mrs Pride, being an officer in the Union, got Monkey Brand to drawing-pin the cardboard notices to the newly erected telephone poles. Notices announcing the teas with silver collections. Cyril stoked the copper boiler, lit the coke stove and in winter trimmed the oil lamps. What Millie would have done without this confirmed churchwarden bachelor no one knew.

Stodge, always good for a joke, said that Master Cyril and Millie both had a bath in a galvanized bath with the water left in the copper boiler. This just added fuel to the fiery feud which always smouldered between Millie and Cyril. Revd Vernon, a desperate man for a bun struggle, as these events were called, started on the ham on one occasion before Millie had time to ask him say grace. The Mothers' Union was not short of women with a sense of humour, and knowing the parson's weakness for doughnuts, bought from Evesham fresh and filled with raspberry jam to go with the homemade cakes, cakes made by competing women who all said their recipe was best. Vernon, sitting at the head of the trestle tables, had a plate loaded with doughnuts placed in front of him. He usually cleared them up, then went to Millie's where they drank sherry out of a silver teapot in tea cups in case of an unexpected abstaining visitor being shocked.

CHAPTER FIVE

Sacco, Sportsman and Naturalist

Sacco's son was born in the Cotswold cottage on the hill. Alice was proud, George Blizzard was proud, the chapel where it was dedicated, with the parents again under the pulpit, turned out in strength that Sunday evening. George Blizzard had not foreseen an easy life for his daughter with such an unpredictable man. His son-in-law took more of the western wine from the apple orchards of our village than was good for any man on a Saturday. His natural musical ability bedevilled him. In constant demand, he played pub pianos until closing time. Alice, strict abstainer, despised her husband coming home so merry, and feared for him as he roared his Norton through the peaceful country lanes of the early Thirties. She locked him out of the Cotswold cottage one Saturday night. Breaking the glass in the door was no problem for Sacco and Sunday morning saw him taking the glass from the pictures on the wall, cutting it to size, and puttying it into the front door. Nothing bothered him, he always seemed to have the answer.

Instead of staying in with the new-born son, Sacco joined the lads at the reading room in the evenings where he took on all comers in the wagon roped ring. He had a punchball in his garden in the pear tree and, stripped to his singlet and shorts, he belted away for hours, the muscles of his arms rising and falling every blow. A five-foot-six man is an unusual sight as a goalkeeper on any football field, but Sacco made it; playing for a neighbouring village team, he could be seen Saturday afternoons fit and agile swinging on the cross bar for high shots and punching the ball clear like he punched the punchball.

Then the goal kicks, well past the centre spot. A classic occasion was when he kept goal in a hospital cup final. A penalty was awarded against Sacco's team. A new rule had just come into force which denied the right of the goalkeeper to move until the ball was kicked. The first time Sacco moved, the ball went in the net but the referee awarded another kick. It happened again. Then the third time the penalty was taken, Sacco stood stock still, the player taking the penalty kicked wide and no goal was scored. Sacco and the referee were mobbed by the opposing supporters after the match but Sacco's prowess with the punchball served him in good stead.

Alice Blizzard, busy in the hillside cottage with her young son, saw little of Sacco in his off-work hours. The whole neighbourhood saw him at the fêtes, racing on foot, on bikes, pillow fighting, on the slippery pole. 'Anything foolhardy,' Gunner said. When he was tired of charging up the village street on his Norton, he was out with Arthur Gibson who had just set up business as milkman in the village. Sacco and Arthur ferreted the rabbits from the hill. Sacco kept ferrets in the lean-to shed next to the privy in his cottage garden, if garden it could be called.

'Who has got the shoot this year?' George Blizzard, his father-in-law, asked him one August when the purple-headed thistles were shedding their blossom like a snow storm and the burdock grew up among the ripening Victoria plums.

'Dost reckon thurs any wild beasts in Sacco's garden?' Joe said to Gunner as together they picked their runner beans. Sacco at the Dragon, primed with cider, told George Blizzard that he had no room to talk of gardening as the only land he would ever possess would be six foot in the churchyard when he was buried.

'Don't seem right for Alice to carry taters from Evesham while Sacco's acting the fool and wenching,' the market gardeners of the chapel said.

Ferrets, like fan-tail pigeons, breed fast and in no time at all Sacco's lean-to was alive with polecats, fitchers and snow white hobs and gills. 'Like a little zoo in there,' Arthur told him as he fetched two useful animals and put them in a sack among the hay to work the rabbit warrens or holts on Bredon Hill. One Saturday afternoon in early autumn I walked up the hill to buy a snow white hob or male ferret off Sacco. As the pink-eyed, quick moving ferrets lapped up their bread and milk and ripped to pieces a dead fowl, they followed Sacco around the lean-to. 'Which one do you fancy?' he asked me.

I looked at the miniature polar bears as they climbed the sides of the shed, fought for meat, for bread and milk, and I replied, 'Pick that one up, Sacco.' Standing there with an empty seed bag I waited.

'Um,' Sacco muttered, the ash of his Woodbine dropping on the floor as he turned. 'Now I have an idea you have chosen a very good working animal, perhaps a little difficult to handle at first but a good rabbitter. Slip it in your bag and give me ten bob and it's yours.'

I wondered why Sacco didn't pick it up. 'No,' I said, 'I'll hold the mouth of the bag open, you pick it up.'

Sacco bent down and caught the ferret with his bare hand across its shoulders, but he was too late, its long teeth caught Sacco who went backwards through the door with the ferret on his finger. I closed the door to keep the rest of his family in and the white ferret loosed his finger and slipped through the thistles towards the Jargonnelle pear tree, perching himself on a low branch. Sacco fetched his boxing gloves.

'You see,' he said, 'what a wonderful worker it is.'

I agreed as the ferret went into his cottage and disappeared up the kitchen chimney.

'Take your pick,' Sacco said, inviting me into his breeding pen again, but having no boxing gloves I decided to postpone ferret buying that day.

The following spring a vixen whelped her cubs in an earth quite near Sacco's cottage. When they were a fair size, Arthur and Sacco dug them out one Sunday morning. The truth was Sacco wanted a tame fox. No Airedale, no spaniel or collie for him, he wanted a fox. The first cub to be within reach in the fox hole was a young dog fox cub. They put it in a sack and took it to Sacco's place. Here Sacco had a cider barrel ready with a hay bed and some of Arthur's milk. After a time he bought a dog collar on one of his visits to Evesham, the hotel and Amy Lights. With collar and chain young Reynard grew up in the barrel by the kitchen door. On summer evenings, I remember the sleek, red, shy fox on the chain following Sacco as he exercised it down to the village. No squire had lived here for thirty-five years, but seeing a man with a bow-tie, hacking jacket and walking stick, walking sedately through the churchyard on a summer's night gave me the impression that Sacco was a superior being – no ordinary mason, a man who surveyed the crops and stock with his red fox at heel. As if he was trying to give the impression why should the landed gentry hunt the fox? Why shouldn't Sacco preserve one for himself? He lived by the earth where they were born; Sacco somehow looked right with his fox. There was none of the head lifting by the tightened chain of the dog show ring, showing off some animal with a pedigree yards long – just a clean-shaven, pink-faced blond man, puffing cigarette smoke, ambling down the churchyard with a loose dog chain and the fox following, alert to every sight and sound of the evening. The stick was not for the fox but to ward off any workman's mongrel, lady's poodle or gipsy's whippet that might attack Sacco's pride and joy. Of course the time was sure to come when the fox would get involved with the local hunt.

As the hounds broke cover one autumn day from the Primrose Coppice, Sacco was taking his midday stroll down the close at the back of the church. It was on a Monday, Sacco never worked Monday. The dog fox tightened his chain and took his master back to their cottage on the hill just in time. As the pack got on the scent they left the hunted fox circling the garden where the dead thistles and burdock of the summer still stood brown under the fruit trees. Alice, petrified by the baying of the whole pack, ran to the bedroom while Sacco and his young cub lay under the kitchen table. It was not until the first whip arrived in his pink jacket that the hounds were called off.

George Blizzard told his son-in-law just to look in the local paper and if the Hunt were meeting at neighbouring villages to keep his fox in that day. Old Harry (Dunn's carter) said, 'We don't want nair another fox caught in Ayshon with a collar on! It happened afore when Harry Fly-by-Night's fox broke his chain. God bless me, some a the gentry went amus mad. They considers this animal of the wood their property.'

As the nineteen-thirties got under way and motor bikes became faster, our friend's long-tanked Norton wasn't classy enough to ride to work on. He wanted something more up-to-date. A quite famous motor cycle racing rider had a T.T. winner for sale. It had been fitted with thick treaded grass track tyres. Sacco bought it – like everything else – on the Never Never. But what a machine to climb Bredon Hill to his cottage all weathers! The throaty exhaust made it sound even faster than it was. Apart from losing half an ear in the station yard as he turned on the loose gravel, going some distance on his side, he had few spills on it. When he crashed in the station yard it meant a spell on the panel under the local doctor for the T.T. winner's rider. Time off work was no worry to Sacco, especially if he could draw sick pay for himself, his wife and his child. He improved, so one fine day he laid out some sacks on his garden and started to give his motor bike a real good overhaul. Just after dinner the bike was all in pieces laid out on the sack bags when a visitor came. A visitor from the Sickness Insurance. A smart lady who had climbed the hill to Sacco's cottage. She inquired off Sacco if he knew where she could find Mr So and So. In other words Sacco, the man she was talking to.

'What a peculiar thing,' said Sacco. 'I was only talking to him a few minutes ago and he said he was feeling better and thought perhaps a little walk further up the hill may do him good. He even said that the Doctor thought he might be able to start work the following week.' The visitor was quite satisfied with what she had heard, made a note in her little book and went away. Little did she know that the person she wanted to interview was the man with his motor bike in pieces and his hands and clothes covered in oil.

CHAPTER SIX

Six Days Shalt Thou Labour

Joe, Emma, Gunner and Mercy with their market garden near the Midland Railway branch line grew crops in succession so that the carrier's lorry called picking up their produce of the land every day.

'Strawberries and asparagus be the crops we specialized in,' Gunner told me. 'You see thurs no seedsman's bills to pay every year. Sparragrass lasts fifteen years or so if it's looked after, the buds coming through the ground as sure as the arun lily makes green the hedge bottoms in February. Strawberries don't last as long as they did when we growed Paxtons but you can reckon on five years fruiting. Then again,' Joe said, looking at Emma, looking at Mercy, 'no mon can pick strawberries or the sparragrass like our two housewives, thur fingers be nimble.'

So in the winter time when the Ganger walked the railway length and the thud of his sledgehammer could be heard through the frosty air to Carrants Field, Joe and Gunner dug the land between the asparagus beds, placing the moved clay like rows of roofing tiles over the crowns below and forming narrow beds with trenches in between. When the heavy clay stuck to hobnailed boots and two-pronged or tined forks, they sowed lime to blot up the moisture from the winter rains for easier digging.

The strawberries were treated a little differently. It is true the land between the rows was dug one spit deep, leaving last season's winter-scorched leaves in mats around the dormant plants. Before digging Gunner and Frank wheeled in their barrows on frosty mornings when the ground would carry a steam roller, barrow loads of rotted pig muck from their pigsties by the brook.

''Tis nature we puts back in the soil,' Gunner said, 'nothing like muck for strawberries with a tonic of kainit in the spring.'

Frank leant on his fork, telling me how 'folks be purging the land with nitre and taking the nature out of it, then it sets like cement.'

While this went on, Emma and Mercy walked the rows of gillies or wallflowers, gathering the few February blossoms or buds, tying them with raffia, then their men wheeled them home on the flat-bottomed barrows of the Evesham Vale to the warmth of their cottages. Here they stood them raffia deep in water in the long, galvanized, Friday-night bath. Perhaps just one hamper for the carrier in a couple of days when the blood red blossoms were cut out and the bunches packed in the withy basket with a few more withy hampers of sprouts to go to market with them. The whole life of Carrants Field seemed eternal, the hazel catkins in early spring followed soon after by the canary-coloured, brookside primroses.

On Sunday nothing stirred in Carrants Field as Joe and Gunner kept the Lord's Day. 'One day more, one day less,' Gunner said, as they walked in their black suits and bowler hats to chapel. Their polished boots squeaked as one day in seven they carried the market gardeners through the morning air to the Bethel on the hill. Here Gunner sat by the harmonium, pedalled and played by Emma, and stroked his cello with the bow as gently as a child stroking a kitten.

'Again,' shouted Frank, if he liked the chorus of the morning hymn, and the music makers gave the refrain as Frank muttered 'Praise The Lord, Hallelujah.'

Frank told us at morning Sunday School of the inescapable sin we had inherited from Adam and of the remedy of the Cross.

'What did the Possle Paul say? . . .' then a quote.

'What did the poet say? . . .' a quote from a well-known hymn.

We were warned of the bottomless pit, the fire and the brimstone of hell, promised a land in eternity where there is no night, nor sorrow, nor crying – a Utopia beyond description for the faithful. Frank declared the wine at the wedding feast at Cana was unfermented like blackcurrant tea. Gunner said that whist and dancing were works of the devil. Cyril Pumfrey took him up on the dancing when he heard him say that at a Parish Meeting, reminding him that David danced before Saul.

'Them as smokes down yer ull smoke in Hell,' Frank said, 'and if we was meant to smoke thur ud be a chimney on top of our heads.'

'A Sabbath well spent brings a week of content,' they told us.

On Sunday nights when the preacher came from away, Emma still filled the air of our bethel with the works of Moody and Sankey. Gunner bowed his cello and other members of his family helped with violins and melodiums. When the time came, before the last hymn, and that innocent looking, blue-eyed boy, Sacco, had passed the collection plate round, the build-up was complete for twenty minutes of warning that he or she who went through that door unsaved may never have another chance to repent but are in danger of a Christless grave, a lost eternity.

The Amens, the Hallelujahs, the Praise the Lords died down. Emma played 'Lord keep us safe this night, secure from all our fears.' What fears? The preacher often put the fear of the devil into us enough to ruin the night's rest of all but the Chosen Few.

Sacco winked at me as he walked along the choir stalls and left the collection plate on the vestry table, and I have reason to believe he liked the world of mortals. If Amy Lights happened to pass on her way to Coney Burrows, Sacco was somehow persuaded in his heart that Amy could not wait to bare her bosoms under the stars, for hadn't the preacher said that the days of our life are three score years and ten (and the T.T. winner could throw him into eternity as he scorched the lanes, sometimes carrying more cider than petrol). Ah yes, the promise of a Better Land was a comfort to the folk who worked Carrants Field, but as for Sacco who had Alice once more in the family way, he lived for the present, yet still keeping Sunday a day apart inasmuch that he spent one hour in the chapel choir for two reasons – one being to please Alice and another that he liked to sing and stay behind some nights and play the harmonium.

Joe and Gunner might have come from the Outer Hebrides the way they observed Sunday. The solemn, undertaker-like face, the dark clothes, the determined walk morning and evening, together carrying the Word – a big black bible – told everyone that these men frowned even at the occasional child passing on a bike. They considered listening to the wireless on Sunday as a road to perdition. It was more of a day of mourning than a day of rest. It was catching and some younger men followed suit.

When the men on the land mowed the hay, the ground dried hard in the June sun. The strawberries and asparagus grew in Carrants Field, the berries of the fruit ripened quickly on scorching days, the asparagus buds shot up like mushrooms on sultry nights. Weekends were a problem to the chapel men. You see, asparagus buds cut on Sunday were kept for Monday's market, bundled with twigs in the cool of the brook, but with strawberries it was different. As the Bedford and Royal Sovereign lay red in the rows, only the birds picked them on the Lord's Day. Joe and Lofty sat on the pitch pine pews of the bethel until the preacher went home. Then they went to their cottages and suffered until perhaps eleven-thirty, when together with Emma and Mercy they walked to Carrants Field, longing for a moon to light their way.

Sitting on the strawberry headland where Sunday's over-ripe strawberries were wet with dew they waited for a distant chapel clock to strike the hour of twelve. On the last stroke, when ordinary folk lay dreaming on their straw and flock mattresses, the Carrant Field gardeners started groping for strawberries for Monday's early market. Not one strawberry must be picked to defile the Sabbath. They groped often under a moonlit sky with finger and thumb and picked the fruit into chip baskets. The carrier's lorry came at six o'clock and as hardly anyone in the parishes under Bredon picked fruit or cut vegetables on Sunday, Monday morning's early market was always the best of the week. As Sacco slept until near lunchtime and never worked on Mondays, he took an afternoon stroll down to the brookside gardens where the partners worked.

'How many nighthowlers cuts asparagus and picks fruit after midnight on Sunday?' he said to the chapel laymen. 'Don't you think you should be ashamed of yourselves, dragging your wives down here when the fruit was ripe on Sunday and you could have picked in daylight?'

Joe was cutting his 'sparragrass' by sliding the steel-pronged knife under the buds until his left hand felt the fracture under the clay beds. Each bud, bunched like fire sticks, lay in the palm of his hand until his gnarled fingers could hold no more.

'Oi, 'tis a queer life on the Midland clay,' Gunner said, groping in moonbeams on a cold June night to provide food for the town folks. 'We picked fruit for a time, then left it to the women to cut the buds which had stood erect and ready on Sunday. We shall get our reward, Sacco,' they said, 'in another world. A world without backache and rheumatics. We prays nightly that thee ull see the light one day.'

Sacco said, 'But I have an inclination that you two gentlemen are carrying your keeping of the Sabbath too far.'

Sacco spoke like that when he wanted to make his point. Working in the houses of professional people gave him a turn of speech quite different from the village folk of the Thirties. For instance, he said to Gunner, 'Where do you get your information in that Black Book you carry on Sundays, telling you to feed your pig on Saturday and not again until Monday? It could well be,' Sacco continued in a sarcastic vein, 'that you do it to put a streak of lean on the bacon when the pig misses meals. Last night I had an interlude with Amy on the hill – that beats all your twelve o'clock strawberry picking.'

'Says in the Word, "Thou shalt not commit adultery",' Joe told him, 'and you know it.'

Sacco with his tame fox at heel and still dressed in his Sunday clothes replied, 'If you study the Scriptures and history you will find out that the commandment you mention was written many thousand years ago on a tablet of stone by Moses when there was not such a surplus of unattached females as the present moment.'

''Tis no good talking to the silly crater,' Gunner said, 'but what with motor bikes and women and Mondays off, 'tis Alice we feels for, her must have more meal times than meals — and the young un.'

CHAPTER SEVEN

New Mown Hay on Washing Day

Harry mowed Pecked Medda, starting early before the flies tormented his horses in the midday sun. As the swathe fell before the mower knife, wet with dew, Harry worked his horses until the six acres were reduced to one and the young rabbits scuttered from the ley. By midday both he and his team of two were in the cool stable, the horses pulling green new-mown hay from the hay rack while Harry with a determination and an inbred skill brushed and curry-combed the horses' shoulders, removing the tide mark of sweat where their collars had rubbed all morning. 'Thur, Gaffer,' he told Farmer Dunn, 'if it kips hot over the wick end, the hay ull be ready for raking Monday.'

Milko had just delivered the morning milk, 'Arthur Gilson,' their midnight milkman, Gunner said, 'only got up once a day and waited for the ground to be aired.' He hitched his horse from the milk float on to his one-horse mower to mow his little meadow by the railway line named The Stocking. As his mower chattered around the field, it slew the moon daisies, the meadow-sweet, in a crop which grew everything except grass. His blond Saxon hatless head matched the buttercups as they lay helpless behind the blade.

'Come on now, we wants an acre down this afternoon, then another tomorrow out of the four-acre, level, winter-flooded field.' The uncut mixture of herbs was dry and tough in the midday sun. As a puff of wind blew, the blossom of thistles followed Milko like a snow storm until teatime when he and his nag sought the shade under the withy tree by his stone-slated cowshed, and Milko gathered a cock of green fodder for his shafted horse while he sat on the seat of the mower and munched his tea. For the first time that afternoon he quaffed tea from the little blue can lid-cum-cup and ate his bread and butter.

Milko watched a hen partridge return to her nest which he had disturbed earlier, the nest where he had left a square yard of uncut grass for her to hatch her brood. It's a wonder Milko saw it among the standing wild flowers. He smoked one Woodbine after another until his already dirty blond moustache turned brown with nicotine.

Next day being Sunday, Gunner's pig went hungry again after he had finished the extra pig wash in the trough from Saturday. Frank killed his cockerel on Monday after he had been seen by church and chapel Sunday-treading Frank's hens. Treading hens on Sunday! The bird hung on Monday morning in Frank's kitchen like a sacrifice – a martyr – for breaking the Sabbath. When Parson Vernon heard of this he told Frank in his kindly way that it was quite unnecessary. 'It's carrying things too far,' he said.

That Monday morning Farmer Dunn sent Tat Steward – one-eyed Tat, who lost an eye hedgecutting years before – down to Pecked Medda with Blackbird (who strangely enough also had only one eye) to rake into walleys Harry's Saturday mown hay. Dozing behind Blackbird, harnessed, shafted to the rake and with loose reins, Tat felt a sudden lurch as the half-moons of his rake scratched a nest of angry, hot-sultry-weather-angry wasps. Blackbird's half-docked stern of horsehair rose erect. Blackbird's ears lay like a squat, formed hare and away they went hell for leather with a swarm of stinging wasps injecting hurtful poison into Blackbird and into Tat who, falling clear of the ugly, half-hooped tines of the rake, lay winded in the untedded swathe.

The wasps followed Blackbird until the eleven-foot wide rake stuck fast in a ten-foot gateway, breaking the shafts and leaving the rake and Tat in the hayfield. Blackbird went to the stable dragging the broken shafts, and as Farmer Dunn met him he was still being pestered by the canary yellow curse of the horses and men of the hayfields.

Mrs Steward did the washing for the gentlefolk, the moneyed folk, the don't-like-washing folks, and that Monday the sails went up on her wire line which stretched from the Worcester Pearmain to the Pershore plum, from the Pitmaston Duchess pear to the Morela cherry. Ghostly white sails of sheets in the June sun. The doctor's pants, artist Tiddley's shirts, all drying for the flat iron of Monday's table.

As Tat limped into the house for dinner, shaken and bruised, Mrs Steward greeted him with these words, 'Bad job this morning, Tat. Had a mishap.'

'Bruised ass like me, missus?'

'Don't be vulgar, what *have* you done? Ain't bin hoss-kicked in the stable?'

'No, fell ass over yud on the oss rake through a blasted wasps' nest in the swathe. Blackbird he bolted, broke the shafts in the gateway. I spicks he's in the stable now. What's thy trouble, missus, on a nice drying Monday when the sun dries the washing amust as fast as you puts it on the wire?'

'Now look yer Tat, if thee ut prop my line up as well as you props the bar up at the Dragon, it would be all right.' She then told him how she had almost loaded the line, just putting the last few things of the doctor's on – his tailless shirts, bandage-robbed of their tails – Tiddley's sheets – sheets where she had to scrub out Tiddley's image dead centre where his five-foot-eight fawn mark showed up plainly where he lay – when the prop snapped. 'It was a good job the gipsies were down Piggy Lane.'

They came every year for the pea picking and camped there. Gippo Loveridge had his summer igloo hooped with withy and canvassed for his family in his usual spot. The peas were not ready that Monday so he and his family set to work peg making. They left a heap of knee-deep withy shavings and made a load of pegs, cutting the metal bands from cocoa cans and fixing them with tacks.

Gippo Loveridge was never short of a few shillings – a few days away from the peas didn't worry him or his family. A family of polite, olive-skinned children from the baby on his wife's breast up in steps to a strong lad, lean and lissom as his father, who had snared a rabbit for breakfast that morning. Wisdom, the father, cut the young shoots of willow in the withy bed, a bed of osiers, the property of the Midland Railway.

Breakfast over, Wisdom started the retail of the white wood pegs. 'Morning Lady,' he said to Mrs Steward. 'You got a nice kind face, could you do with a few pegs this morning?'

'No, Wisdom,' she said, 'but you be just in time to give a hand with my clothes prop.'

No sale for pegs, he thought, as he looked dark-eyed at the face of Cuckoo Land's washerwoman. 'Tell your fortune for nothing, can't be straighter than that.'

'All right then,' and Mrs Steward wiped her red washer-woman, Windsor-soaped hands on her blue and white apron.

'There's a lucky lady,' Wisdom said, 'You'll be a grand-mother before the year's out – a blue-eyed boy.'

'How did you know our May was in the family way, Wisdom? You've seen her, you rascal, walking big-bellied up the street.'

'God's honour, Mrs Steward, we been down the lane, all our people, until today peg making. But your prop's broken. I'll get you another one, honest I will.' Wisdom Loveridge walked back down Piggy Lane to the withy beds, leaving his pegs at Tat's wife's house. He walked the withies stalking with his bill-hook, not looking for peg withies or even rabbits but for a nice, straight, forked pole of ash or nut for Mrs Steward, strong enough to hold the washing of the upper-class of Cuckoo Land. Two swipes with his bill-hook and down comes a piece of Midland Railway property. 'They won't miss a nut pole – Mrs Steward's in a plight this morning.'

Back at Steward's laundry garden Wisdom puts the new prop under the wire line making safe the week's washing. After Mrs Steward had told Tat of her morning's trouble and Tat had eaten an uneasy dinner during the telling of it, Mrs Steward said, 'Now, Tat, let's have a look at what you have done to your ass.'

Tat let his broad falls drop on to the kitchen floor and his wife rubbed in embrocation, the same as Dr Overthrow used – a mixture of turps, linseed oil and beaten eggs. This made Tat dance as drops of the lotion stung him almost like the wasps in between his legs. 'Damn it, ooman, I bin stung enough by them wops. Whurs the blue bag?'

Out of patience, Mrs Steward replied, 'Handy, of course, unt it wash day?' With the bag she dabbed the stings on his face and neck and eased the pain. At two o'clock Tat left the house to borrow a rake to finish raking the Pecked Medda. Mrs Steward ironed her weekly harvest of whites and coloureds on the scrubbed kitchen table. She heated her irons on the fire in the oven grate, sweating from the heat of the flat irons as they glided to and fro.

Tat with Mr Dunn hooked Blackbird into another rake, keeping well away from the angry wasps that day to finish raking. George, Harry and Mr Dunn then took a wagon into the field to pitch and load the made hay. As they passed Tat with Blackbird, George said, 'Dost know to find a wops nest? I knows a bloke as wants some maggots for fishing? And thy face, Tat, thee looks as blue as any Tory. I allus thought the missus used the blue bag on the whites.'

'Thur ull be a part of this ground I'll give a wide berth to with Blackbird. You chaps can please yourselves, them poisonous sods won't puncture me no more today.'

The jingle of the harness and the creaking of the wagon wheels, the snorting of the horses, were the only sounds in the hay field except for the usual backchat between George and Harry. 'Old Tat combed that nest out good and proper. I see he has left a good piece unraked around it, that ull be a guide when we get there with the wagon.'

After tea, part-time men came with Dunn's other wagon and loaded. Jim Bradfield rode the trace horse from meadow to rick yard, his heels dug in the traces like stirrups. Mrs Dunn sent frail-baskets of sandwiches down to the field, jars of cider, as the men went home at dark with the last load of the day.

Jim rode the foremost horse, the frails hung on the hames and Harry carried the empty cider jar. Ungearing the horses in the stable, Tat came in with Blackbird first, then the swinging traces of Jim's horse, the spreader, catching the stable door as he shouted, 'Hold up thur,' and the brass tops of the hames just touched the lintel as this seventeen-hand gelding went to his stall. The cart saddles hung by cruppers on wooden pegs, the mullins hung on smaller pegs on the harness house wall. Then the long grass or tracer harness; hames first, then back band, hung damp with sweat in the ammonia-scented stable. It was night.

CHAPTER EIGHT

Narrow is the Gate

The footpath to Paris where we played hoops and tops was well worn. For centuries labouring men, women and children had walked the grassy track each day. The action of leather soles, hob-nailed boots, kept the turf in condition; it could have been the green of a golf course. But it was straight and narrow, clover covered, a bit of turf the sheep kept to when they grazed Church Close and Boss Close and moved from field to field. Two gushing springs from the hill were crossed by the footpath just short of Paris. At the lower end it meandered through the tombstones of the churchyard, two feet away from my grandfather's grave, then under the copper beech and the yew tree that stands underneath it like a labourer sheltering from a thunderstorm, then on past the spring snowdrops, purple crocuses which, with lady smocks later, possess the land between the stream of spring water and the row of drooping ash trees. Drooping ash trees reputed to have been planted by grandfather and the Bakers, and then through the lych gate, a modern construction of unseasoned oak with gaping cracks matchbox wide, but the whole structure covered with mossy Cotswold tiles, a harbour for country couples late at night, and barnward-bound, cider-sodden pea pickers were often benighted on the bench seats. The eaves by the cross hung low over the kissing gate (slip slap gate) by the side of the main funeral gates. When the gate was constructed with its overhanging roof the people of Paris, like most ordinary people, had growing families. Their access to the village was through the lych gate, formerly a pair of iron gates. Through here they pushed their baby-laden, shopping-laden prams coming home from town or village shop.

Cyril Pumfrey locked with a padlock the two gates under

the tiles. Millie Bostock told him how wrong he was to block a right of way. A right of way for the villagers to take their prams and bikes.

'You shall no longer borrow my broom to sweep the churchyard, Cyril,' she told him. 'You have worn every bristle off two already.'

Cyril sniffed, lit his pipe and keckled, shrugged his shoulders and replied to Millie. 'Look here,' he said, 'Milko's cows often wander the streets day and night and graze the roadside verge, then stray into God's acre and undo the work I've done tending the beds of the dead.'

'More bones of mine up there than yours,' Millie replied, 'and another thing – I don't like the way you keep chipping the path wider, nor making double graves look like marrow beds. When I'm gone, I'll be in the family vault so you will have no need to cut the daisies over me.'

Millie opened her gate by the cross and allowed all the prams and bikes up her garden and out of the little gate at the top, back on to the footpath. This satisfied Millie, she had company when the shoppers passed, but it did not satisfy the Parish Council, especially when the captain of the church tower banged his head as his six-foot-two frame tried to get through the slip gate for bell ringing practice one winter's night. The Parish Council wrote to Cyril asking him to unlock the gate. As stubborn as ever, he refused. The District Council took the matter up with similar results. Then a representative of the County Council, with Parish councillors and the District Council surveyor, met Cyril at an arranged meeting in the lych gate. The surveyor pointed out to the church councillor that the man who received the blow from the overhanging eaves would have had a perfect right to smash the lych-gate lock to give him access to the churchyard. Most unchristian, the chairman of the Parish Council called Cyril, but all Cyril did was to get his barrow and excavate another foot of soil from under the eaves so that the tallest man could use the kissing gate without a blow on the head from the overhanging timbers. Stodge said he didn't know why they needed a gate – 'Nobody wants to get in thur and nobody can get out.' Cyril sniffed, smoked his pipe. The gate remained locked. Cyril held the key, only releasing the great padlock and chain on Sundays, for weddings and funerals. Stodge told him as they stood together on the bit of grassland where God's acre, as Cyril called it, met up with Council property in Stodge's keeping, 'It don't become a Christyun to behave like thee dost. If thee wast to read the Bible instead of eyeing Millie and wearing out her brooms a sweeping all the churchyard rubbish, 'fetti and all into my road, it ud be more to thee credit. Ast ever read whur it says "Remove not the ancient landmark which your fathers have set up"? That right of way is a landmark and little does you care for the mothers and young uns at Paris. I'm a telling you, Cyril,' Stodge went on, 'if the old squire had bin alive and he maintained that yer roadway belonged to him 'cause he owned the housen and land anant it, bless the fella, he'd av peppered thy ass with shot if you had locked that thur gate.'

Cyril sniffed, keckled, shrugged his shoulders, stuffed his hands deep into his trouser pockets, telling the old roadman to cut the hemlock on the corner and make the village look as if somebody owned it. Then turning sharply in his ox-blood boots he offered Stodge a pipe of tobacco adding, 'I admire your spirit but you are wrong. The gate must remain locked to keep out Milko's cows.'

CHAPTER NINE

Rubies and Midnight Milk

Arthur Gilson, known as Milko, rose at ten every morning, hitched Blossom in the milk float and tying the harness to the shafts with string where the straps were broken, drove down Piggy Lane to milk his four red Rubies of Devon. 'A sight for sore eyes,' Stodge said, as his ramshackle turnout bounced and bumped past the mounting stone outside the old blacksmith's shop, a stone where many a plough boy had climbed on to to mount the newly shod shire horses of the village. Milko had four useful cows in the meadow by the railway line. His cowshed, stone-tiled, was primitive. An earthen floor, wooden mangers, muck-stained, just the faint remains of whitewash left on the walls, but Milko wasn't fussy. If the cows stood quiet on the field and he talked quietly to them and took the bucket and stool and milked them where they stood. In fact it was much cleaner in the fields and with one bucket of water from the brook he washed their udders with an old sack bag then, throwing down his Woodbine, pushed his greasy cap-covered blond head into the cow's flank and sat on the three-egged stool. *Chee, chow, chee chow,* the milk rang in the steel pail until froth rose like the head on a pint of beer to the three-gallon mark on the bucket.

'No milk like Milko's,' he said to himself, as he tipped the bucketful into the churn in the float where Blossom waited patiently until milking was over. 'Ah,' he thought, 'one of my best customers on the round won first prize at the Baby Show with a boy reared on my milk.' The cows stood and chewed their cud while their teats were squeezed by Arthur Gilson.

Front two teats first, then to the back, and finally stripping the last drop with open fingers instead of clenched fists. As Blossom fidgeted he shouted, 'You wasted life, do you think I stole you.' In winter when the wooden manger was filled with the mixed herbage of Milko's hayfield and he handed round the cattle cake like the vicar handing oranges to the Sunday School treat, his Rubies stood still ankle-deep in mud and muck and Milko's stool sank deep in the mixture.

Up Piggy Lane when the farm men were carrying their empty frail-baskets home for dinner and the village children bowled their hoops and whipped their tops down the road past Stodge to school, Milko's float bounced over the rough stone track with his first delivery. Blossom knew just which house or cottage to stop at, so with the leather reins tied to the short brass rail on the front of the vehicle, Milko dropped the tailboard, grabbed his pint measure and once more tipped the milk from his churn to his bucket which he carried up and down the foot paths through the garden gates to find the jugs, basins, preserving jars and, it has been said, new chamber pots standing outside the front doors.

'What time dost call this?' Gunner asked him, as he came home for his one o'clock. Gunner, who had been back-bent, hoeing, digging, picking fruit and vegetables since before the sun peeped over Broadway Hill, said, 'Why should a man get up in the morning when he has the health and strength to lie in bed?' Milko replied, 'Thee bist just as gaumless as Sacco. Dost ever read the Book?' Gunner looked at him with a look of anger, yet in the bottom he was sorry for Milko and Sacco. 'Go to the ant thou sluggard, consider he ways and be wise,' Gunner quoted. Gunner was always quoting.

Milko sank his measure deep into the foaming milk, poured Gunner a quart into the jug. Blossom had halted neatly by Stodge's barrow outside Joe's house. No one came to the door but a glance from the dinner table was enough to assure Emma that the first lot of milk straight from the Red Rubies of Devon was on the step. Milko picked up the coppers from under her preserving jar and put them in the greasy satchel slung from his shoulders and her quart was scooped from the bucket with the pint measure. Just a dash extra for Emma, Milko gave. 'She pays on the nail,' he thought, 'not like some who want it on the strap.'

Up at Coney Burrows, Milko paused as Blossom trimmed the green shoots off the hedge. 'Not the usual jug this morning, bit of nice Worcester,' he thought, as he turned the quart porcelain over. 'It's old by the marking. I've heard Father say that Dr Wall's work is valuable now-a-day. I'll tell Flora Lights when I see her.'

On jogged the float until the last customer was served. 'About a quart left in the churn,' he thought, and pouring it straight into his pint mug, his tobacco-stained whiskers on his two lips parted as he drank the dregs of the morning. 'Do me as much good as anyone else,' he said to Stodge, who was again at his never-ending task of siding, stockaxe or jadder flailing the roadside turf, then sweeping the overgrown verge up and into his barrow.

'Dare say,' Stodge answered, 'and unt it time to pull them cows' teats again?'

'Look here, Stodge,' said Milko, 'if the Government decides to put the clocks forward an hour in the summer I don't go along with them. I always keep to God's time.' Stodge gave him a look, picked up his stockaxe and continued working.

From four o'clock onwards, after washing his churn and buckets at the standpipe tap by his house, Milko did the work on his holding, mended a gap in the hedge, dug a few potatoes. But Blossom remained in the shafts tied to the Burgundy pear tree at the top of Piggy Lane, dozing, knowing that the next journey down to the cow ground would be by lantern light most of the year round. Milko milked at about half-past nine to ten at night. At this hour, when Gunner and Joe lay beside Mercy and Emma, the churn clanked, the bucket rattled, as once more Arthur Gilson rode in the float lantern-lit, moon-lit, to pull and squeeze the tits of his four cows.

Nothing stirred in the village apart from a few talking outside the Dragon. A whispering courting couple stood where

Blossom had stood under the Burgundy pear tree. Milko had the world to himself at night; the puffing of a late-night goods train and the sparks from the engine's chimney, a dark silhouette of the fireman shovelling coal from the tender as he opened the fire box and for just a moment the footplate was illuminated.

The rich red Rubies, Milko's reservoir, stood in line waiting for the night owl of a master to come and ease their udders. They could not chew their cud in comfort under the withies until the second milking of the day had been gone through. 'Get over, Cherry,' echoed in the still air as Milko put the tie chain round her neck. As the T went through the last link and she nodded her head up and down from the manger to the hay rick, her sharp straightish horns missed Milko by an inch and the chog (square of wood) rattled against the manger. 'Over, Granny and Peasbrook, over Ruby,' and the milkers stood now four feet apart under the Cotswold roof which lay so heavy on the timbers. 'Let's have it now,' he said to Cherry, as his head felt the kicking of her unborn calf. The milk squirted into his pail as he thought, 'I'll have to dry her off soon now. Give her a rest before she calves. Ah, about three parts of a gallon,' he muttered, as he tipped the frothing milk into the churn in Blossom's float. The lantern hanging from a broken plough trace lit the shed in an eerie fashion, casting shadows. Shadows of cows, of buckets, of beams, of Milko. Turning the wick up a bit and unhanging the light from the trace, Milko looked carefully at Granny's bloated bag. He felt it, found it to be hard and a bit inflamed after her recent calving. 'Don't want no garget among my cows,' he muttered to himself, and reaching instinctively for the salve he rubbed her udder. Granny lifted her hind leg in a half-hearted kick and Milko drew the milk into his pail carefully. Standing there as the church clock struck ten, the lantern hanging once more from the trace, Milko was not really afraid of a kick from a udder-sore cow but more afraid of losing two gallons of precious milk. The chains fell off one by one from the cows' necks as Milko once more had the churn ready for delivery. Up

Piggy Lane again the float jolted over the stony road, Milko sitting on the lid on the churn, the lantern hanging on the head board of the float. The glow of his last Woodbine neared his whiskered lips and he threw down the butt end. Outside Gunner's his midnight song started, always the same, spring, summer, autumn and winter – harvest hymns, deep and rich like a church organ. 'We plough the fields and scatter.' Mercy turned on the feathers of the double bed, whispered to Gunner. 'Must be nigh on midnight, thur's Arthur's anthem.' 'It is fed and watered,' Milko continued.

'I hope it unt watered,' Gunner muttered.

'Milk-hoo!' Arthur's voice rang through the midnight air, Blossom once more doing the rounds.

'Unt thur no rest for any on us nights? For goodness sake, what dost want to make that nation noise for?' nightshirted George Blizzard called from his bedroom window. Flora Lights came down in her sweeping nightgown, stood in the porch. 'Later than usual tonight,' she said, as her quart jug was filled. 'You are generally here about ten to twelve. Have you seen Amy, she hasn't come home?' As the night-spirited men and the maiden ladies opened their mullioned windows and listened to the end of 'All is safely gathered in,' Milko heard a stir in his garden among the plum trees. He had just washed his churn and pail under the standpipe, leaving four pints at Revd Vernon's (he, sleeping the sleep of the just, had left a note on an old envelope 'four pints Milko – visitors tomorrow'). It was Sacco and Amy Lights canoodling in the garden shed. The cider-happy mason greeted Milko quoting Tennyson, 'Sunset and evening star, and one clear call for me, and may there be no moaning at the bar when I put out to sea.'

'No doubt there will be some moaning when you get home to Alice,' Milko replied. Then eyeing Sacco and Amy Lights in the hovel doorway on the owl-hooting, cat-fighting night, Arthur spluttered through the glow of the lantern, 'You greedy devil, Alice has room for you to bed down on the hill and here you are with Amy.' Clutching Sacco's arm, Amy tittered and whispered to Arthur, 'Seen our Mum?' 'Yes,' the milkman said, 'she is nightgowned at the door, the Ganger's asleep. Some folk have all the luck. Take me for instance. Only one of the last male descendants of a family who have farmed these acres four hundred years. Forty years of age I am – no wife, no children, the family will die out . . .' He unhitched Blossom from the shafts and the milk cob trotted down to the little meadow in front of his house.

Before Sacco revved his motor bike up the hill in the small hours, he told Milko that if it was a woman he wanted, he would find him one in Cheltenham if he got the old Gillette to work on his beard and maybe bought a car. As Milko rolled into bed that early morning, he thought of the legion of Gilsons who had ploughed and sowed, reaped and mowed since Queen Elizabeth came through his village. 'Bringing in the sheaves,' he said quietly. Then even Milko was asleep. No, not the daily round; just milk at midnight.

CHAPTER TEN

Bread and Wine

'Break thou the bread of life dear Lord for me.' So sang Joe, Gunner, Mercy and the members of the Cause to the chapel harmonium as the group sipped the unfermented wine from egg-cup-like glasses once a month. For the folk of the Established Church, it was a sixteenth-century chalice passed round, brimful with Sacramento. The nineteenth-century vicar J.E. Linnell, a native of Silverstone, declared often during his ministry in Northants and Bedfordshire that 'If God ever laughs, and I'm sure he does, it's when he sees his children refusing to meet at his table.'

One has often thought in this way as the folk living at the top end of the village walked to church at the bottom for the bread and wine, while many from the bottom walked with Joe and Gunner to the top chapel for the same reason. Rising at six on a Sunday for Early Communion Linnell declared a mistake, 'For it's the Lord's supper, not the Lord's breakfast,' he said. But bread and wine are symbols of life itself and however misguided folk may be, if it's comforting to conform or not to conform, all well and good. Sacco never took the Sacrament at chapel; I think Joe and Gunner would have frowned on this. Sacco was uncommitted, independent. Convention meant nothing to him.

Bread in Ashton was eaten in quantity by the men on the land in the Thirties; with potatoes it was the staple diet. There was a choice of at least four local bakers. Our village baker, Mr Stallard, stood sweating at the bake-oven door handling the wooden peel like the oar of a boat and using it shovel-like to bring the excellent bread out of the oven. Batch cakes, cottage loaves, the long since forgotten four-pound loaf, dough cakes. To recapture the smell of fresh-baked bread of that age is to bring back in memory days of sunshine from early morning till late at night, of the lightly sprung baker's cart waiting with scrubbed shelves to receive the unadvertised product of stone-ground flour and yeast, the tempting crust which no boy could resist sampling from the batch cakes. An impatient cob called Express daily drew the cart to the Bredon Hill villages.

If one wanted to taste bread as made by grandmother, an occasional loaf from the mill on the River Isbourne, reputed to be the only river in England to run due north, was a change. The old men said this bread had more stay, satisfied the appetite for longer. I believe the miller put a few boiled potatoes into it. The bread from Beckford was to my father's taste. The main bakehouse there produced a loaf similar to Stallards but rather less doughy. The golden crust of the unsymmetrical loaves ebbed over the main loaf in a kind of range of hills. As the wicker basket hung from our porch, the loaf on top soon lost its ridge of crust as I returned with bulging satchel from the four-twenty train from school.

But Careful Sammy was the man to remember. A short man with black polished leggings, trilby hat, tweed coat, clean but frayed at the sleeve edge, frayed at the breast edge. His clothes were weathered by being constantly in sun, wind, rain and snow. His basket made of withy twigs was as battered as his hat. The upright twigs stood up naked like spikes, the handle mended with sewn calico, last week's *Journal* filling the holes in the bottom. Sammy's turnout was too heavy for a baker's round. His cob was more of a half-legged cart horse and would have looked more in place in a coal dray. The dray itself was like the covered wagon on the Atora Beef Suet advertisement. The hooped top, gipsy style, and tarpaulin did cover it, but the draught from the front to back must have been terrific. The sheeted top was lashed with ropes to the tailboard but the front being open, the wind whistled past the sack seat of Sammy and out of the back. The horse was darker than a liver chestnut but could not be described as brown. Painted in white on the black tarpaulin were the words 'Sam Hicks, Baker and Corn Merchant, Poultry Food a speciality.' The clip clop of Sammy's horse could be heard long before he arrived in the village those Saturday mornings when an extra train on the line got everybody speculating 'Where the 'scursion was to' and the roads were as quiet as a public library.

But why Careful Sammy? Everyone was careful in the country. Cabbage water went in the pig wash tub, little bits of soap were muslined for the wash day. Sammy was an honest to goodness baker. He had probably known Pinchloaf, the one who sold underweight many years ago. The dray was spotless, a rack of scrubbed deal carried the bread, the fowl corn, the sharps or middlings for pigs and poultry were at the back near the tailboard. A short man like Sammy needed a step to climb on board his dray. From here he reached his loaves off the rack, loaded his basket and fastened the leather reins of his horse to the front of the tilt above his head. The horse stopped at just one *whoa* from the baker and started when he clicked his tongue. I suppose Sammy delivered in about four villages. Our village was his limit northwards and he came Wednesdays and Saturdays. Every bit of string that fell off his meal bags was preserved, his bags were patched and mended until very little of the original remained. Mother had a loaf every Saturday, more out of kindness than anything because his bread, although wholesome, was underbaked, anaemic Dad called it, but there was a nutty taste that was quite pleasant when it was about two days old. Careful Sammy kept pigs in his horse field. He bred Middle Whites and sold the weaners at eight weeks old to the cottagers. Sammy's pigs always did well, he fed them well, although I shall never forget going to his granary and watching him shake the empty meal sack so that the fine sharps – middlings or barley meal – fell on the stone floor where he swept them up carefully into a bucket for his sows. Fifty shillings was a usual price for his weaners forty years ago and a bucket of meal salvaged from the customers' sacks robbed none. When he emptied the sacks into the cottagers' bins, the village women would not have thanked him if he had created clouds of meal dust by beating the empties like carpets over the bin. Someone once cut a piece of

Housing for the Romanies

Viewing the land

A rare possession

The baker

Village church and church on wheels

The blacksmith

Ferrets — and now for some rabbits

Outside the inn — a welcome break

string from around one of his sacks and he was upset, saying that he had had the same piece of string for years. So the sight of a sheath knife appalled him and many is the time the cottager's wife has stood for minutes while Sammy untied a difficult knot in the string. Coming to our house one day with half a hundred-weight of barley meal and making a special journey of four miles with it, he arrived at the door with the receipted bill which he gave my Mother. 'Now Mr Hicks,' she said, 'I have the receipt so there's no need to pay.'

'Ah but Mrs Archer,' he said, 'your name is worth more than six shillings, isn't it?'

An interesting man was Sammy. One day when he was reckoning up at a neighbour's house he was interrupted by her husband coming in to dinner. 'Nice day after all, Master Hicks, although it was a smartish frost this morning.' Sammy, in the middle of his sum, said, 'Quiet please, George, let's attend to the business first.' When the little account was settled, then and then only, would he discuss the weather, politics or religion.

It's sufficient to say here that in Sammy's day a baker's shop did smell like new bread. This yeast aroma had nothing more chemical, more synthetic about it than the scum from the beer or barm, baker's yeast and good wheat flour. No thermometer told Sammy, Mr Stallard, or the others how hot to get their ovens; it was just an inborn instinct like a country woman sticking a knife in her cake to see if it was done. The bakers of bread were master men, men who did nothing else apart from dough cakes and cooking Christmas dinners for families in their big ovens and drying home-cured bacon in their chimneys.

The winemakers were mostly women. They made wine out of anything, recipes handed down from mother to daughter. Kate Dunn's beetroot wine equalled a good port, Millie Bostock's cowslip was as smooth as silk. The great thing about all this fermentation of fruit, flower and sugar was its unknown strength. Some home-made wine, which was just like drinking milk, was sly and got many a man in trouble with his family when he got home. Plum Jerkum, that wine of the Pershore plum, can be very strong. It can have a quarrelsome effect on man. In the cottage in those days glass jars stood in the small windows behind the check curtains. Jars like large goldfish bowls where little bits of stuff like cotton wool rose and fell to the bottom of the jar. Known as bee wine, the bees having to be supposedly fed with sugar pretty often, the honey-coloured liquid fermented until when bottled it was sweet and, according to the strict chapel abstainers, non alcoholic, but was it? It made many a countryman say more than his piece after dinner. If wine gladdens the heart of man, that's a good thing. If it makes him unreasonable, bad tempered, well, it's just undesirable.

CHAPTER ELEVEN

Water Music

'Here we have no continuing city,' Revd Vernon told Emma as she sat by Joe's sick bed.

'Ah, Old Joe's a filling a water, he ull last about a wick,' George Blizzard said to Harry (Dunn's carter). 'Comes up from the legs,' Harry said, 'and once it gets to the heart it's curtains.' Joe, a stalwart at chapel, was on the way out. Sacco visited him. Sacco always visited the sick. As the horny hands of the market gardener lay brown and withered on the white sheet, his eyes lit up when he saw Sacco.

'My days are numbered,' he whispered (so that Emma couldn't hear). ''Tis water trouble,' and quoting from 'the Word' by his bedside said, 'Man is born to trouble as sure as the sparks fly upward. You have seen them, Sacco boy, at Harris's blacksmith's shop.'

Sacco put his cool hand on Joe's heated brow and knowing that Emma knew the worst turned to her and putting his arm around her waist led her to the dormer window in the thatch where the apple blossom flowered in the orchard below. 'Very shortly,' he said, in his semi-professional manner, 'Joe will be crossing the River Jordan. You know that, Emma?'

She nodded her head. 'You have never seen the light as we have, Sacco, but it's our wish that you help to carry Joe to his burial.'

'Of course I will,' Sacco replied. 'Didn't we build the chapel wall together when I was apprenticed as a mason?'

Joe beckoned from his bed, and Emma put another pillow under his head. The furrows in his weather-beaten face looked deeper, his white hair cropped and parted down the middle gave him a look of great character.

'Yes, Sacco. You have never seen the light and it's bin my

wish you would have done before I meet my maker. Take my bible and read it. See where John 3, Verse 16, is marked with my name and when you sees clear as I did put your name alongside.'

Next evening in the Dragon, Ganger Firth greeted Sacco as his motor bike brought him home from his work on a Worcestershire church. 'Have you heard the news? Another stiff un up the road. Old Joe's gone.'

Sacco straightened his bow-tie, looked pensively into Cooper's fire and said, 'Joe was a good man. A man as never abused himself. Just pass my cap round for Emma, and Ganger, you can help me to carry him and we don't accept money being he's a friend and native.'

'Joe's gone and we have got another youngster on the way,' Sacco said, as he started his first pint of Cooper's beer. 'It's a very strange thing it happened like this,' he said.

'No good thee a-making excuses, no good shutting the stable door when the hoss is bolted,' Tat Steward, whose wife had had more children than days there are in a month of Sundays, laughingly said, and he added, 'Them as has the pleasure of getting um has the pleasure of keeping um.'

'You know Cyril Pumfrey's brother?'

'What the hell's it to do with him?' Ganger Firth butted in.

'Wait a moment and I'll tell you,' Sacco went on. 'Cyril's brother Kenneth, who comes from the Black Country, has been busy fixing wireless sets in the village. Two Bradfield boys help him. They climb poplar trees and fix aerials, dig holes and sink old buckets in for earth wires. I have a three-valve wireless set made and fixed by Kenneth.'

'What av that got to do with Alice being in the family way, I caun't see,' Harry said.

'Neither can I,' Cyril said. 'You can't blame Kenneth for that.'

Sacco looked in pity on Cyril, saying in a superior voice, 'Of course we must all have sympathy with Mr Pumfrey for if he had coupled with Millie Bostock years ago as I told him, he would understand.'

'Out with it, we can't listen all night,' the Ganger said.

'It was like this,' Sacco continued, 'at Christmas I fixed an extension speaker, one like an old gramophone horn, on the set and took a long copper lead up into the bedroom. As you people who understand music will appreciate, Handel's finest composition was the *Messiah*. I listened to the *Messiah* in bed — some choral society sang to a fine orchestra and there we were, Alice and me, drinking in the music, the bass, the tenor, sopranos and the altos. When it came to the Hallelujah chorus, folks in the audience usually stand, like they did at the first performance years and years ago. You can guess the rest. Nature being what it is, Alice and I were both satisfied that Christmas night, so about Michaelmas our wire clothes line will be pegged with three-cornered pants.' Sacco went on, 'Now, about this funeral. Emma's pretty shaken, I'll see Revd Vernon. There's Ganger an me; what about you helping to carry, Tat?' Tat nodded approval. 'One more, Arthur Gilson. He can help in between milkings.'

Stocky the sexton tolled the bell on the funeral day — passing the bell, to be exact. Mr Gregory, the undertaker, met four of Cooper's customers in black suits, green with age, black pancake caps, outside Emma's cottage. Everything was black, even the sky looked black. Mr Gregory's pony and harness was black, tied to the greening walnut tree. The four men reverently manoeuvered Joe's mortal remains down the steep crooked stairs. Sacco at the bottom end with Milko took the weight and then in the garden the coffin was placed on the wooden-wheeled bier, the work of a master wheelwright whose stone stood by the tower in God's acre. Gregory with top hat, black-gloved, as solemn as a judge, an expression learned by years of this sort of thing, walked with arms slightly swinging ahead of the four bier-wheeling men of the village. As the flower-smothered carriage crept silently down the street, silent apart from the noise of the boots of undertaker Gregory and the four bearers, all curtains were drawn at the cottage windows. Men and women stood with children, dogs and horses, the men bare-headed holding their workaday caps in respect of Joe. 'Man that is born of a woman hath but a short time to live and his life is full of misery,' Revd Vernon recited at the church yew tree. 'It's not all misery,' Sacco thought, as Amy Lights came down the path.

Back at the cottage, the bearers refused any money from Emma for their hour's task. Sacco and Milko ate fishpaste sandwiches, two at a time, drank tea out of the chapel urn, ate plum cake.

'Unt like it was years ago,' Tat Steward said quietly. 'We allus buried 'em with ham; allus kept a ham for the purpose slung on the bacon rack along uv the chines salted in case of a christening. And drink. They drank the dead into the ground, it was thought a respectable thing to do.'

But Joe was gone from his market garden, leaving Gunner to work it alone. The chapel was poorer by Joe's passing, the land was poorer and the village was poorer. Sacco thumbed Joe's bible at his hillside cottage and Alice's time got nearer to producing what they hoped would be a girl and made a pigeon pair.

CHAPTER TWELVE

The Grape Vine

Before the early nineteen-twenties, the telephone had not reached our village, neither had Cyril Pumfrey's brother installed wireless sets; we were dependent on the papers which came on the eight-ten to the village to bring in news from the world outside.

It was as well to record here that there was opposition to the telephone, not from the natives but from the settlers from Birmingham, who looked for beauty and art and decided that telephone wires and poles had neither. Ten subscribers eventually had the phone installed. The wireless was rather different, Gunner and Mercy deemed it as 'works of the devil' and refused to clip on the earphones, not even to hear Big Ben strike six o'clock. Cooper at the Dragon had the loudest set in the village, a five-valve affair with a half-hundred-weight low tension battery and aerial high on the top branch of his walnut tree.

It was not that the people in Ashton wanted splendid isolation, it was that we were of low rateable value and of little consequence to the county. Sacco listened intently to Charlie Kunz and impersonated him on the pub piano. Ploughboys sang 'There ain't no sense, sitting on a fence, All by yourself in the moonlight.' This underdeveloped village and its people, apart from a few retired city gents, had never heard music apart from village concerts. The church held an affair known as the Parochial Tea where men of the Great War sang songs from the trenches. Ladies who had been to festivals at Cheltenham sang with men of the choir pieces by Gilbert and Sullivan. Millie Bostock sang to her own accompaniment 'Come into the Garden Maud'. The scope was so limited. Gramophones with great horns scratched records by Caruso. The wireless changed it all, as Sacco found when he listened to the *Messiah*.

Down at the station along the branch line from Evesham to Ashchurch stood telegraph poles with wires in between. Wires which sang in the wind, buzzed and oscillated. In the room marked 'Booking Office, Private,' the Morse code was tapped out on the board. The head porter and the underporter took no notice of these pips and squeaks until they recognized their own particular code calling Ashton Station. Then and only then they listened for the telegrams which came every day. These messages in Morse from faraway places were written down on forms printed for the purpose. The forms were folded in little buff envelopes and despatched to their destination by the underporter, full speed on his bike. You see at the top of the form it noted time handed in, time received, and it was assumed that if the wire or telegram came from a distance it had to be tapped out several times before reaching Evesham and on to Ashton. It is funny that Gunner and Mercy didn't consider telegrams as 'works of the devil'. When one arrived, as it often did, delivered by Tat Steward's son, underporter, telegraph boy, sweating on his bike, saying 'Load gillies, cabbage, onions, tomorrow – Clark, Sheffield', Mercy was pleased. Then there were the ones to the farmers like Dunn which read 'Expect cattle at Beckford Station on the five-twenty' from a Shropshire vendor. But when young Steward went to a labourer's cottage that was different. The women hanging out the washing, Stodge the roadman, Cyril Pumfrey and even little Monkey Brand Pride watched as the cottager's wife slid her finger to open the sealed envelope. 'Wonder what's on then,' Mrs Steward would say across the hedge to Miss Badger. 'It is to be hoped it unt bad news for Flora Lights,' Stodge said to Cyril. Cyril sniffed as if anything to do with the Lights family was suspect. 'It's from Lil, bless her,' Flora shouted to her neighbours. 'She's three months gone but the soldier at Worcester where she now works is marrying her directly.'

'Flora seems pleased,' Milko told his customers as he delivered the milk.

'Oi, as pleased as if her had found a Titty Obbins nest,' Tat

Steward added, 'and Flora bin telling us the last time as her was home that Lil had got a tumour. Mind,' he said, 'the Ganger's a better mon along a Flora than ever Harbour was. Allus delicate.'

'My poor old aunt at Nottingham has passed away,' Kate Dunn told Millie and was overheard by George Blizzard who remarked to Harry, 'Thur's a funny thing – passed away – my relatives allus died. Some be called and some falls asleep according to the stones in the churchyard, but mine have allus died most on um natural like.'

Then Tat had a wire, 'Please meet me off the seven o'clock, I'm coming for a week. Loving sister Elsie.' 'That's the missus's sister from Brum,' said he. 'Shan't get a word in edgeways now. They allus comes when my plums be ripe, thur's no doubt the guardsvan ull be loaded with plums and runner byuns. Still her allus brings us a bit of ham from the market hall.' Then there was the news which came from Tewkesbury Market on Wednesday, or Beckford on special Tuesdays when the landlord could not sell cider because he made more profit on beer.

The Sunday School outing to Weston kept the village informed of the state of the crops in Somerset. 'Hay as black as a soot bag,' Gunner told Arthur Gilson. 'You be lucky to get your herbage in a yup and thatched a straw.'

Outside the church gates on summer Sunday nights the doings of the week were put through a fine tooth comb. The state of Sacco's garden; Toodles who had bandy legs; Flora and Ganger; the goings on of Amy Lights. Outside the chapel wall, as Sacco slank from the choir, the few master men there gave their orders to the workers. 'Start pulling the mangolds tomorrow; move the cattle from the Leasow to Spring Hill; or tell so-and-so to be early in the pea field to keep the crows off the Lincolns.' Then, 'What did you think of Mrs Blizzard's hat?' and 'Emma, don't you think it's early for her to go out of mourning for Joe?'

Then news came from Evesham Fruit Market by the carrier with his lorry which had replaced the horse and dray. He brought news of the day's prices at Market, the political situation as seen through the eyes of the market gardeners. Village people must have something to talk about. Sacco romanced in his stories of Tewkesbury and Stratford-on-Avon when his motor bike pulled up at the Dragon. He had always seen something out of the ordinary. He told extravagant tales of driving his machine so near to a motorist changing a wheel in the road that he took the seat off his trousers and without hurting the motorist. But Sacco's T.T. winner was soon to be replaced by a push bike. Alice and two children to keep, then there was the drink he treated his friends to as long as he had a penny piece. So Sacco was forced to join the majority of the workers by going to work on a push bike. Going shorter distances, the grapevine suffered.

CHAPTER THIRTEEN

Milko's Car

'Our family has been in the village for six hundred years and looks like dying out,' Milko told Cooper's kitchen customers at the Dragon. 'What shall I do about it? I'm forty years of age and have no children.'

Tat Steward blew the top off his pint, Cyril did his usual shuffle from one foot to the other and sniffed as if it were indecent. Flora Lights, who was present that night with Ganger, said, 'I'm sorry I can't oblige, I've had my quota.' Amy Lights offered her services for a consideration but refused to bear any children. 'I have my clients to consider.'

'Damn it, Milko,' Sacco said, as he'd said before. 'Get a car and I'll find you a woman in Cheltenham.' Milko bought a car like buying a loaf of bread; he paid for it in sovereigns which belonged to his grandfather. He drove it, a custard-coloured tourer, down our street with Sacco as his tutor. Dressed up in their Sunday best they made for Cheltenham. Their Woodbines puffed smoke, the car with an exhaust made from old carbide tins puffed smoke. Sacco operated the handbrake when necessary and as the Sunday night darkened and the gas lamps lit one by one, the old lamps of Milko's new venture showed the way to High Street and the Moon pub. Sacco vamped the ivories of the piano, Milko drank the Cheltenham Ale and in no time at all a girl stood there. Stood there ready to change some Victorian sovereigns from Milko's pocket. Twice round the Gas Works and Milko had a date – a date every Saturday. 'Nice to have a chap with a car,' Eva said. 'Are you a farmer? I see hayseeds in the back.'

Sacco associated with his usual doubtful women of Lower Dockum. He told them the same old blarney of how Tewkesbury Abbey would have fallen down had it not been for 'me and my old chap'. The cows in the meadow down Blacksmith's Lane were tight in their udders when Arthur Gilson eventually milked them at 3 a.m. 'No good waking the village tonight,' he thought, 'I'll give them extra milk tomorrow.' So that night the jugs and basins and jam jars were wet with the morning dew and stood empty on the door step until the vendor of milk decided to deliver the two lots together on the Sunday dinner time. Saturday nights in Cheltenham proved quite expensive to Milko. His Victorian sovereigns were swallowed up by his friend's extravagance with the women and the beer. The 1913 Humber was always going wrong – so different from Blossom and the float. Again, Sacco appealed to the girls so differently from Milko. His china blue eyes, dapper appearance, confident manner, his chat about anything under the sun, landed him with a dark-haired street hawker's daughter, the Lower High Street Venus. 'A real brawmer,' Sacco said. Milko's partner was the one who had leant on the pub piano for years, just a sponger who attached herself to Arthur Gilson because of his bag of sovereigns, his car with brass headlamps. Marriage and the perpetuation of the Gilson family was far away from her thoughts. 'I suppose you know that Eva is "one of them",' some hefty navvy told the milkman one Saturday night. 'You are just one of the suckers who keep her.' Milko was disillusioned. 'Sacco's such a nice man,' they all said, 'he plays the piano something beautiful.'

The hawker's daughter who sold flowers in the Prom was well-made, well-dressed, a kind of mixture of gipsy and Mediterranean type. Large black eyes, bosoms like watermelons, firm and erect, supported her black dress quite as much as her sleeveless shoulders did. Sacco's Alice with two children on the hill was timid and quiet, lacked the spirit of her husband. As village folk said that Flora and Amy were anything but what they should be, Alice was pitied, the mason described as 'gallus'.

As the midnight milking was not done until Sunday's early hours and the Humber became a burden, Milko sold his car to a scrap iron jack one Saturday night. Often he had driven home alone, leaving Sacco for a night in the Spa. Now with the sale of the car and the milkman's journeys to Cheltenham to find a partner to have and to hold having proved fruitless, Sacco could see that Saturdays in town would mean eleven miles to cycle each way. The motor bike was gone and Milko's Humber was gone.

Oh! the dark-eyed beauty held Sacco in her spell for a while. Milko milked his cows late on Saturday nights again while the mason and the hawker's daughter stayed late at The Moon, spent summer nights on the half-built ricks of Tewkesbury Road and winter nights in the house of her father. A house where artificial flowers for the street trade filled the sitting room. The daffs, the tulips, the watercress, stood in galvanized baths in the back kitchen. At home, Sacco's garden became a wilderness. He sold his ferrets, his piano, his fox went to his brother-in-law's and Alice, who never knew when he was coming or going, grew despondent, deciding it would be best if they parted. Sacco still went home to tea on Sundays, sang in the chapel choir, then to the Dragon piano as if drawn by a magnet. Once he had heard a tune he played it without the music.

Milko's car driving was short lived. Blossom, faithful Blossom, stood shafted to the milkfloat for hours, waiting for her twice-a-day trip down Blacksmith's Lane. Sacco spent some nights in Cheltenham until his work took him to Stratford, but he had no permanent home in the village until Farmer Dunn and his sister Kate fixed him up in the harness room of their nag stables. Here was a fireplace, a mantle, a window adjoining the nag stables now used for Dunn's carthorses. The harness room, with iron saddle-shaped fittings screwed to the wooden walls to hang the saddles on, iron bridle-shaped fittings to hang the bridles, had been used as a bothy by the groom to eat and sleep in, to attend to a foaling mare. Sacco painted his new retreat, and ordered half a ton of coal off coalman Drinkwater. Kate Dunn found him a bed and table and chairs. He bought an old piano at the Smithfield, was given a cottage organ by his sister-in-law. Cyril Pumfrey's brother fixed him a wireless set and Alice, depending on her sisters and brothers-in-law, went quietly on bringing up the children.

To comment on the situation would be wrong without knowing the facts. Sufficient to say that Sacco and Alice were as unlike as chalk and cheese. Milko's car and his exploits with the Cheltenham piece were just the last straw to separate the pair.

CHAPTER FOURTEEN

The Harness Room and Naomi's Cottage

When depression strikes the Western world as it did in the early Thirties, men on the land, the countrymen, although deprived of the little extras which made life more tolerable, suffer less than the town folks. Here the employers were strict in an almost Victorian way, but they kept their men. Bona fide farmers took to market gardening when the corn trade slumped. Agricultural labourers were careful with their twenty-nine shillings and threepence per week. They grew potatoes, snared rabbits and with their wives gilly picking in the spring, pea picking in the summer, blackberrying for sale in the autumn and wooding in winter, they got by.

Sacco, when he worked as a mason or helped Milko with his dairy farm, had not the money to spend each evening at the Dragon. Naomi's Cottage was a primitive Working Men's Club or Boy's Club. At fourteen all the village boys sat around her open fire and in turn bought the wax discs for her gramophone. Drinking mugs of thick cornflour-laced cocoa, smoking Woodbines at twopence for five, here the winter evenings were whiled away. Sacco came up from the harness room and played Naomi's piano. If you believe in witches, Naomi was one. Bent and old, on two sticks, a hooked nose and one very long tooth, in the lamplight of the eerie building which lay alongside Painting's barn, the ceiling saffron with ages of fire smoke, His Master's Voice horned gramophone spun the terrier to the tune of 'Ramona', 'How Long has this been Going on', 'Horsey, cock yer tail up' and the like. Evenings when the solitude of the harness room were forgotten in the din of Naomi's cottage, where her love child who never grew up mixed with the boys, toasted rounds of bread to go with the cocoa, and where the huge pickle jar of onions and cauliflour was stabbed of everything except the vinegar by the nineteen-thirties dropouts of the village. Then the select few – Milko, Ganger, Tat – went along with Sacco to his hideout and sang to his cottage organ. Sacco had been reared on Moody and Sankey at the chapel, so the strains of 'The Old Rugged Cross' sounded through Dunn's stable while Ganger totted out some cider he bought cheap, four and a half gallons at a time, from Stallards.

'Been in the Kings Arms while we worked on the main line today,' Ganger said. 'Nice drop a beer at dinner time.'

'Never liked the place,' Tat answered. 'I went thur years ago with a hoss when I worked in the stables. I remember it well. I'd had a gutsful of mushrooms that morning for breakfast, ketchupers as big as dinner plates, they played me up. The jolting of the cob was too much, I had to walk.'

'What's that to do with the beer?' Milko said.

'I was coming to that,' Tat Steward went on, 'we drunk out of pewter pots and I never did care for um, give me the earthenware mugs every time. Ever bin in the Kings Arms, Sacco?' he added.

'No, I have never been in that establishment. I'd very much like to be in the Queen's arms, but I doubt I should get too excited.'

'Women again,' Milko said. 'Didn't we learn our lesson down at Cheltenham?'

Back at Naomi's as Naomi's love child changed the needle, two of Gippo Loveridge's dark-haired daughters came one night. They sang to the gramophone, clicked their heels on the kitchen flagstones as they danced, their plaits swinging around their heads and long earrings rattling like peas in a can. Sacco winked at Milko. Tat and Ganger were unmoved by the gipsy's inviting Gippo Loveridge to go with them to the Dragon.

'Turn the gramophone off,' Sacco said, just as Naomi was going to wind it up once more. 'These girls will sing better if I make the ivories dance on the old piano.'

Milko leant against the mildewed mahogany of the instrument standing, Woodbine puffing, close to Sacco on his battered stool.

'Plenty of old tunes under the stool,' the keeper of the club said.

'Thank you, Naomi, but there's music in my heart tonight,' and starting with a chord the mason played 'She was lovely and fair as the rose of the summer, but it was not her beauty alone that won me.'

The girls' voices blended, there was a kind of open air feeling to the olive-skinned Loveridges in their singing; it was as if the larks were going up for the very first time on a February morning, a morning when the fog lay in the Carrant Brook meadows and the pale sun with so little power lit Bredon Hill and only the blackthorn shone white in the hedges and the elder pale green.

'Again, let's have it again before I milk.' Arthur Gilson had been lifted for a few moments by the lilt of the Loveridges. 'The red Rubies can wait a while tonight,' he said.

Then under the deal settle Naomi's son found a bottle of Ganger's cider. 'Tot out for the girls,' Milko told him, 'the wood smoke will make them dry-mouthed tonight and come to think of it I'm dry-mouthed myself.'

So the drinks stood in odd cups on the piano top and as they drank so the voices at Naomi's soared higher, just like the larks. A knock at the door proved to be Amy's brother late again with the *Echo*, the evening paper. Naomi squawked through her one long tooth, 'What time dost call this? half-past eight last night, nine o'clock the night afore, now it's nigh on ten.'

Sacco's eyes fell on the girls in the yellow paraffin light of the kitchen, moved from their shiny black shoes to the aproned waist, the fancy coloured blouses holding the ample gipsy bust, the dropped earrings, the black, jet black, plaits, their placid eyes beneath the plain black hair ribbons. He closed the piano lid and turning said, 'This village is no place for two of the most beautiful of God's creatures to go alone to

Blacksmith's Lane at ten-thirty. Milko, you have Blossom tied to a telephone pole, come in the float with us to the milking sheds.' The lantern-lit float jogged up the rough road and while Milko held the reins, Sacco sat between the two Loveridges.

'Not since the day I was vaccinated by Dr Overthrow have I seen such a pair of girls in our village,' he said.

'All our people are dark and handsome like our father is. We live a healthy life, not like the Cheltenham women I've heard you gentlemen have been with. Ganger told us all about it and the motor car.'

The red Rubies were milked in the small hours once more as Milko tied Blossom to the pear tree and the four unattached suddenly became attached as they strolled up Bredon Hill, forgetting all about the Rubies, the Harness Room, the masonry on the abbey. The girls forgot that early next morning they would be shaving the withy sticks into pegs for the washing line while the iron pot was slung over the fire. A pot filled with poached rabbit, onions from Gunner's small-holding, potatoes from Mr Dunn's bury, while a saucepan full of late peas simmered by the side. It was just another night for Sacco. A night of love. For Milko, whose legs shook at the thought of being alone with a woman, it was excitement as the midnight hours passed at the Cuckoo Pen with a silence which fitted the occasion. A passing goods train on the branch line four hundred feet below showed her red fire box, a whistling plover crossed on the way to the marshes, an owl hooted from the clump of beeches and down Blacksmith's Lane flickered the gipsies' fire close to their hooped tent.

Again the midnight milkman delivered the two milkings together, as his float brought the evening milk slushing in the churn over the cobbles at four in the morning. But the two harbours where music, love, dancing and card playing went on were the Harness Room and Naomi's Cottage.

CHAPTER FIFTEEN

Recreation Room and the Village Bus

Village life between the wars when the last train left town at seven in the evening was still the parochial existence of grandfather's day until the motor car and the service bus came. It's true that Mr Cambridge had his Sunbeam car and his son had an engine and dynamo to light his house with electricity, but it was still the age of paraffin lamps and dripping candles and chamber pots. 'Dumb wells', George Blizzard called the septic tanks of the progressive with W.C.s and baths.

The Room, or Recreation Room, as it was called, a wooden army hut from the First World War, was a social centre for the graduates from Naomi's cottage. Here the click of billiard balls could be heard as they crossed the bright green baize under the powerful Aladdin lamps. The shirt-sleeved youths of the village vied with their elders chalking the cue, potting the red. Others played quoits, dominoes, then out of the blue a new caretaker was appointed by the Secretary, Cyril Pumfrey. A naval man, a friend of Cyril's known as the Admiral by all, lodged with him. He tricycled down the street every evening to open the Room. The Admiral had been an instructor of the Noble Art, in the Navy. In Harry the Carter's words, 'he could use um'. Nothing, he impressed on Cyril, is more important that the Science of Defence. Here Sacco, Milko, Ganger Firth spent some winter evenings having boxing lessons from the Admiral. He demonstrated the body blows to the solar plexus, the upper cuts, how to cover up, lead on the opponent, and furthermore he knew the tricks in boxing which often went unnoticed by the referees. For instance, he showed Sacco how, when he parried a blow, diverting it above his head, it was easy to bring up the right elbow, lean foward and deliver an unpadded elbow to the chin. This in itself was the break up of the boxing classes. Sacco used this trick on Ganger Firth one night as they stood toe to toe in the waggon-roped ring. The Ganger of the railroad, whose sheer weight and muscle could almost have knocked the side out of the room, turned on Sacco and taking no notice of the Admiral's whistle for the end of the round, punched Sacco out of the ring, breaking a window with his head.

But as few villages had such social centres, how did this place under Bredon get theirs? Mr Cambridge gave it, his father paid to have it erected by a local firm of builders. That was in Ponto's time. Ponto the man who slept rough, worked in people's gardens, held pigs at the killings, picked mushrooms and was almost drowned at the Dragon when Wisdom Loveridge and his boys held him the wrong side up in Cooper's water butt. Ponto was the key man in the building of the Room. The building chaps were very thirsty that hot summer in the Twenties. Ponto carried cider with a yoke and two buckets from Dunn's and they drank it as fast as he carried it. In between times he did carry water to mix the cement mortar which went into the joints in between the bricks of the piers it was to stand on. It's always been debatable as to whether Ponto carried more water for the building works or cider for the men; sufficient to say our Room was built on cider. The felt roof soon let in the wet when the rain was heavy, but just at that time the Admiral heard of a shipload of corrugated iron sheeting being salvaged in the Straits of Dover. The cargo ship had been torpedoed in the last part of the war and was now being refloated after some years on the sea bed. Army and navy stores all over the country were quick to buy the sheet iron, sheet iron which was covered with sea salt. The salt destroyed the galvanizing to the extent of making the material rough, but it was still galvanized iron. Cyril bought a truck load and once more the builders roofed the Room. Once more Ponto carried a few more buckets of cider from Dunn's cellar. An outside Gents was made with sea-salvaged iron and local withy.

Sacco was proud of the Recreation Room. He did odd jobs for Cyril to improve it. He built a Ladies convenience as a lean-to of iron and withy. He erected a heavy lead water tank to catch the rain-water from the spoutings so that when it rained the Ladies had a modern flush toilet.

The billiard table, a present from a Knight who gained his title through his efforts in equalling out the food for the Midland counties during the First War, was full size on huge bulbous legs. Visitors to the village, when they saw the table, or perhaps played on the table, were amazed at its perfection. Ironed by the Admiral, the green baize would have been quite acceptable to Joe Davis or even Walter Lindrum.

Sad to say in later years, when the naval man was unable to tricycle up the lane and be the custodian of the Room, a man took over who lacked the discipline and the way with the young men that the Admiral had. Soon boxing developed into punch-ups; then some youth who had nothing better to do, cut the green baize on the table with his sheath knife and the club ended. The table was used to form the foundations of a stage for the infrequent amateur dramatics. The Recreation Room stove was no longer lit nightly in winter, the oil lamps with their yellow light, the Aladdin with its mantle shining white over the billiard room, hung cold on the cross beams.

Millie Bostock still gave Mothers' Union teas, Monkey Brand carrying the water. Cyril Pumfrey was jealous because it was a well-known fact that his visits to Millie's cottage ended when he saw some other man's photograph on the piano. Cyril organized Whist Drives. These were conducted with immense respectability. The Room trustees had made a rule that no intoxicating liquor was ever to enter the premises. Here the chapel and the Dragon were at one because the chapel welcomed this because of their principles, the pub because it would lose them no trade. So at weddings if the couple were toasted in champagne, it had to be at the school. Only the odd chapel goer went to the Whist Drives, the majority believing that the hearts, clubs, diamonds and spades were the works of the devil. Church folk went, Cyril Pumfrey being M.C. He, being brother-in-law to the vicar, made a rule that no whist playing should take place in Lent, so on every Pancake Tuesday, whist was finished until after Easter.

It is said that Mrs Collins at the shop had a sharp fall in sales of sugar during this period when the villagers drank their tea sugarless. No dancing in Lent either, at the Room. Cyril saw to that. It seemed that just at the time of the year when folk needed a lift after the winter and before the spring, this denial was to some extent senseless.

When the old cinema closed in Swan Lane, Evesham, the Scala was built in the High Street. During the day we were served by trains on the branch line, but George Anderson, motor engineer who at one time drove steamers on the Avon, now saw possibilities in providing a village bus. His first effort was a Model T Ford which he converted from a lorry to a covered vehicle with benches both sides and a step at the back. The seating was for about eight, but it took more as he started for town at six o'clock on those Saturday nights, coming back when the pictures were over. This provided a long-felt want for the young folk. During the day and in the week it went to town with shoppers, loaded at the back end with small market gardeners' produce and returning with the empty hampers. Sacco met Amy Lights in Evesham and together they sat on the plush seats of the Scala to watch Charlie Chaplin and *The Kid,* Mary Pickford, Douglas Fairbanks, while the little orchestra in front of the screen played suitable music and the drums rolled and cymbals clanged at the vital moments. Soon, of course, the talkies came and Sacco, the nonconforming nonconformist, sat with Amy, enjoyed the love scenes and, learning nothing he did not know already, was aware that Lofty and the Elders, Emma and Mercy would be appalled at bare bosoms, stories of deception, of unfaithfulness. Flora Lights went on the bus with the Ganger and often George

Anderson had to wait while the man off the railroad swallowed his last pint.

But the Model T was fast becoming too small for the villagers and to everybody's surprise an announcement in the local paper one Friday gave the story entitled 'Built in a Bedroom'. George Anderson had made a bus partly in a bedroom. In no time at all it was on the road. The Brown Eagle, a twelve-seater with the seats comfortably upholstered by Mrs Anderson, matching curtains, in fact a luxury bus for that time. By shoving up a bit, a twelve-seater could hold far more on a Saturday night and packed to the door, one could hear in there all the local news without buying a paper. 'Mrs So-and-So is having another babby.' 'That ull be five, won't it, Mrs Jones? . . . .' 'Gunner's peas av all bin utt be the jackdaws. . . .' 'My Lord, old Master Dunn as lived here yers ago, father of the one at the farm, left a smart bit a money. . . .' 'I say that's a nice bit a mate from Byrds, unt it? . . .' George Anderson puffed at his pipe, dropped passengers at their doors. To say he was responsible for many marriages and births would be true, but deaths – no, because over the years from the Model T to the Brown Eagle, George at the wheel always got his passengers home safely. He no doubt heard more village talk on those Saturday nights than in the barber's shop.

CHAPTER SIXTEEN

Parsons and the New Sexton

As Revd Vernon was Low Church Conservative – Evangelical if you like – Miss Curtiss often went to a little village half-an-hour's walk away where the rector, a bachelor, was Anglo-Catholic. Revd Driver was a wealthy little man who drove an old bay pony in a governess cart. A good visitor, they said of him, and very generous to the ailing poor. 'Different to Master Vernon belly-wise,' Stodge said. 'Vernon ud yut anybody out of house and home. Didst ya yur about the strawberries?' he said to Harry as the carter's snorting horses grazed the battered grass verge on the way to the meadow.

'Noa, I beunt one to pry,' Harry answered.

'Well, prying or no, I was told as how Vernon went to tay at Gunners and they plugged and washed two pounds of his best Royal Sovereigns and dammed it he didn't yut the lot bar four. Gunner and Mercy did manage to get two a piece.'

Revd Driver often brought Miss Curtiss home from service at his church and Harry said that 'Her had better watch her step cos he ull be a feeling her pulse else.'

'Parsons be like doctors, they never yields to temptation,' said George Blizzard. Harry laughed, adding, 'They be a damn sight worse than they calls the laymen 'cause they does no work – afternoon sort of men I calls um.'

But Driver was a saintly man – an old-time countryman who studied the flowers, the birds and the crops – a cut above Vernon. The incense of St Cuthbert's, the brass, the bowing at the altar, prayers for the dear-departed and to the Virgin, suited Miss Curtiss to a tee. She lapped it up like a puppy at a saucer of milk, but her eyes were set on Revd Driver.

'Such a nice man, so well brought up,' she boasted to Millie Bostock. 'You shall come to tea with him one day in the week. I've invited him for Wednesday.' So Millie tightened her corsets, put on her navy silk dress and in her many-times-trimmed hat and veil walked sedately to Miss Curtiss's cottage where the governess cart stood with its shafts pointing skywards in the side drive, and Donavon, the pony, was tied to the manger in her stable.

'So nice to see Millie,' she said to the man of the cloth, 'she does do the flowers so well at St Barbara's.'

Introductions over, the silver teapot spouted tea into three cups.

'Sugar, Millie, I just forgot,' Miss Curtiss said.

'Two lumps,' Millie said, a little acidly.

'The rector and I don't take it, do we, Mr Driver?'

'No, no, Miss Curtiss. But I must tell Miss Bostock what a nice church you have here though I would miss the polished brass eagle forming our lectern.'

'No popery at God's house here,' Millie said.

Miss Curtiss took this as an insult to the devout bachelor, and said sharply, 'Now Millie, no criticism of St Cuthbert's please.'

'Please,' said the little rector. 'Our differences are of no importance if we have the right spirit within.'

'Apart from Vernon's appetite bordering on gluttony, he does conduct himself according to the Prayer Book.' Millie coloured as Miss Curtiss said this, and Miss Curtiss saw that Millie was jealous of her bachelor friend and realized what a mistake it had been to ask her to tea. 'I'm playing the organ now at St Cuthbert's,' Miss Curtiss went on.

Millie looked at the rector, then at her hostess. 'Encouraging popery and being unfaithful to our church,' said she.

Miss Curtiss grabbed her half-full cup of tea and threw it across the table at Millie, who walked sedately through the front door under the flowering clematis, and home. The rector was nonplussed, 'Really,' he said, 'in all my years in the

Ministry, I've never had this happen before. You are coming with me, Miss Curtiss, to apologise.' Harnessing his pony to the governess cart, he drove down the village after Miss Curtiss had taken the uncut cake as a peace offering. As the three sat around the mahogany table at Millie Bostock's house, the Revd Driver spoke of immediate reconciliation between the parties and advised them to say nothing to the members of St Barbara's and St Cuthbert's. Often Revd Driver brought home Miss Curtiss but she remained friends for life with Millie, so once again Revd Driver was the perfect peacemaker.

'I'll have to resign the grave digging,' Jasper Hill told Vernon after a funeral one day. 'It's me bones, they gets stiff and I was born too soon.'

'Quite, quite,' Revd Vernon said. 'You will still pass the bell, I presume, and carry the candles and say Amen at Service.'

'Oh oi, I'll do that, Vicar.'

One Monday when Sacco was getting over the weekend, walking dressed-up to the Dragon, the vicar said to him, 'You are a versatile sort of chap, Sacco.'

'Potent, you mean?' Sacco replied. 'Yes, still potent and hoping to remain so.'

The vicar laughed. 'That's not everything, Sacco, but could you be our new sexton? Dig the graves — your job is such that you can take half a day off when a parishioner leaves this earthly scene.'

So Sacco took on yet another service to the rural community under the hill. 'But Vicar, I seem to remember an epidemic of influenza just after the war; they were burying every day that spring. Now if such a thing happened, I couldn't cope, not with the mason's job, my pint at the Dragon, and Amy.'

The Vicar said it was most unlikely, but that he and the churchwardens would be responsible. It was a hard winter, Sacco's first as sexton. 'Some calls me the Verger or Virgin,' he told Millie. 'I doubt if you would qualify with Cyril around.' Millie blushed, saying that she had never been intimate with any man and believed that Cyril had never been with a woman.

Sacco was just taking the turf off for a new grave, pegged and strung the shape of a coffin. 'Before you enter those Pearly Gates you and Cyril should experiment with sex. Why not?'

Millie, looking at Sacco, said, 'That has been the main thing on your mind ever since you ravished Martha.'

'Yes,' he said, 'and did you know that when we had our cot on the hill, Alice and me, her young sister used to stay weekends. I persuaded Alice to make an early morning cup of tea on Sundays, then I slipped into bed with her sister. You only live once, Millie.'

'Everyone shall give an account of himself at the Last Day,' Millie said.

But soon, funerals to Sacco were busman's holidays and as the ground of the parish churchyard had been buried on before, he acquired coffin plates which he polished for his harness room brass. He made coal scuttles decorated with the things he dug up. Once he dug up a golden denture. Revd Vernon told him to replace it and not rob the dead. Then he found a shallow box which his predecessor had buried. He called the vicar who said, 'Oh dear, cover it up.' Sacco's Woodbine ash dropped on the clay as he said, 'Vicar, if the live won't hurt you, it's a certain fact that the dead won't.'

'How dids't get on today a-burying Harry's mother?' Ganger asked him in the Dragon.

'As a matter of fact, I buried one and throwed two out. That ground is full of bones – back to the Battle of Tewkesbury.'

CHAPTER SEVENTEEN

Battle at the Dragon

We knew that the notice barring peapickers from the pub applied to all except Wisdom Loveridge and family. When the evenings were cool in early September the two garden seats under the apple tree in Fred Cooper's garden were a poor resting place for the tired pickers. Fred Cooper had been ailing for some time. An acute turn of sciatica had put him to bed for a week or so. Sacco helped in the bar. The peapickers arrived from up the Gipsy's Lane, a whole drove of scrap-iron jacks, scissor grinders, peg sellers, horse copers, at the Dragon that night. Sacco stood in front of the XX marked barrels with their wooden taps, drawing pints of beer. The cider in the flagstoned taproom he measured in the pint crocks from the half-hogshead barrel. Cyril Pumfrey drank bottled stout.

'Have a couple of pints of cider, Cyril, and put some lead in your pencil,' Sacco grinned a toothless grin. 'We a got company tonight,' Tat Steward said to Gunner as he looked through the window. 'Don't thee let um in yer,' he advised the temporary barman. In front of the gang walked a tall girl, powdered and rouged and wearing a white dress like a bridal gown. She was ashen blonde – not one of the Romanies. Sacco's eyes sparkled as he met her in the doorway. 'You see the notice,' he said, 'your friends ud better drink outside.'

She looked appealingly at Sacco, explaining that the caravan people were very orderly and would give no trouble. They all came in, mostly men, swarthy men. The horse copers wore check waistcoats and tight cord trousers. They were orderly and their womenfolk sat together in the corner near Tat.

'The lady in white, she is not one of your people?' Tat said.

'No, she comes from a gentleman's family, but joined us in the peafield,' Tat was told.

As Sacco drew the beer and cider he had difficulty in keeping his eyes off the stranger, often spilling Cooper's special as he left the tap on too long under the barrel. Cyril talked to Milko and as he fingered the silver band on his pipe he muttered, 'Sacco is taking a risk tonight.'

'Who's the lady?' Cyril asked the sexton. 'One of your fancies from Cheltenham?'

'I'm surprised at you noticing her, Cyril,' he said, 'but confidentially, I would rather sleep a night with her than with you.'

Cyril sniffed, keckled, turned to Milko disgusted. 'He's no fit person to stand behind that bar,' he said.

Then, about three-quarters of an hour before closing time, when Tat, Stodge, Harry the carter, Gunner and Milko had had nearly enough for the night and the travellers with the lady in white were talking faster, bragging about their horses, their waggon, their wives and children, the sound of horses' hooves and caravan wheels could be heard coming from Elmley way. As the little convoy drew near the Dragon and the sleepy-eyed, sun-tired children poked their grubby faces, grubby but healthy, from under the hooped vans, the lurcher dogs close to the back axle and the women suckling their babies for the ten o'clock feed, the men left their horses in charge of the boys and trouped in line towards the Dragon. These people were not the cosmopolitan crowd from Gipsy's Lane but direct descendants of the people who came over from Europe with their horses and vans four hundred years ago. Sacco stood in the doorway and once more said, 'No travellers inside the bar', but seeing the girl in white and recognizing her as one who had once travelled with them, they entered.

'Watch it,' said Wisdom to Tat. 'I can smell trouble,' and in no time at all an argument broke out between the two parties. Sacco, remembering his boxing training at the recreation room, squared up to one party, only to be howled down by the women who screamed, swore and blasphemed. Hearing this, the caravan women outside came in and the hair pulling and the wrestling got out of control. The lady in white was sheltered by Sacco. Spit and sawdust flew across the room when the men hurled the spittoons at each other like cricket balls to the wicket keeper. The locals hid behind closed doors in Cooper's living room. 'A smack aside the yud by some of that ironwork and Sacco would be planting some on us among the yew trees afore our time.'

Amy Lights, coming by late from a date, rode her bike and fetched the policeman. By the time he arrived the pub was empty and the womenfolk flocked round the local policeman like wasps around a jam pot. One difference though, they made much more noise, each woman trying to outdo the other. The policeman managed to persuade the Romanies to get on their way and the woman in white, the tinkers, the scissor grinders, horse copers and their womenfolk returned to the pea fields of Gipsy's Lane. Blossom waited patiently for Milko and together they went to draw the midnight milk in the meadow of the Rubies. Sacco got Ganger and Tat to help him sweep up the broken crocks and glasses. The sawdust was swept from the bar floor and once more the spittoons were in place ready for another day when the twist-chewing Ganger, Tat and Harry smoked and chewed and spat over their deliberations about life in the village under the hill. Next morning Sacco mended the one broken window at The Dragon and painted with a steady hand the notice 'Peapickers and Gipsies served only outside.' 'I wonder where she came from and where she is going,' he said to Cyril about the 'Woman in White'. His china blue eyes twinkled and Cyril knew what was on his mind.

CHAPTER EIGHTEEN

The Hopes and Fears of 1930

In 1930 when Britain groaned under the weight of the great depression, millions lined the dole queues and children of the streets ran ragged and barefooted in the industrial north and South Wales, the countryside under Bredon was relatively better off. It is true that George Blizzard, Harry and the rest of Dunn's men took home twenty-nine shillings and threepence for fifty-two hours work. Sacco, if he wanted work, could earn six pounds as a tradesman. The Ganger, Firth, was considered well-off on about two pounds a week. The whole point was that there was almost full employment. Smallholders like Gunner led a precarious life, dependent on wind and weather, drought and flood, to make a return on their crops, to give a little margin over expenses. This took no account of hours and hours of work by Mercy and Emma. Mr Dunn no longer grew wheat but turned to stock raising. His argument was that by rearing calves they were bound to grow into money. The farmworker after paying his rent had little left to buy the sevenpence an ounce Red Bell tobacco but grew potatoes on field headlands, scrogged the apple orchards after the pickers had finished and stored enough for winter dumplings. When a man is on the breadline he improvises. The first few motor cars of the immigrant insurance men, dentists and retired Army officers often gave a lift to the Saturday shopper who could ill afford Mr Anderson's bus or the train to Evesham. The men bought meat from the Argentine at a little shop up Port Street, Evesham – beef at fourpence a pound if they waited late on a Saturday night – and they walked home with a full frail.

Fresh vegetables were always available as the sprout fields spread from the Vale of Evesham to Bredon Hill and beyond. By working hard George Blizzard's sons could earn ten shillings a day picking for market. It is not true to say that the years of the depression were not felt in our village because for a honeymoon period after the First War, wages and conditions had been reasonable. Milko made his two rounds a day with his milk but now some folk turned to buying skimmed milk from Kate Dunn who made butter for market, some bought cheap condensed milk. Every week in the season of colder weather when the rabbits squatted on their grassy formes on Bredon Hill, men carried stones or a hammer in their grey fustian working coat to throw at the rabbits on their way to and from work. Most cottagers had a stew jar on the hob or in the oven with a turnip from the sheepfold, a few of Gunner's carrots and onions which made a mid-week meal for the family.

It is difficult to compare the lot of town and country in those days. Monkey Brand Pride, some years retired, did a bit of fruit picking to earn his rates as his shares went down. Cyril Pumfrey could no longer spend so much money on the churchyard and had to be reimbursed by the Parochial Church Council. But as Stodge chewed his twist then dried it in his tobacco tin to smoke later and men robbed partridges' nests for eggs, shot wood pigeons for meat, there was a satisfaction. I am sure that the village folk were content to a great extent. There was little money for clothes but to see George Blizzard on a Sunday in Tiddley Chandler's, the artist's, cast-off suit was a sight to remember. Tiddley was a tall man with a long body, George was a short and square one. On Sundays, when the sun bore down on the browning grass of the Nap, George's trousers reached almost to his armpits and his braces held them there. Even then the turnups of the Harris Tweed were well down on his boots. The women fitted themselves up at rummage sales but the children often had their clothes handed down in the family and to see a well-dressed child in 1930 was a rarity. Boys of fourteen left school for the plough driving, but the ones that got away went by cycle to Evesham as apprentice hairdressers or lather boys. They made good.

It was fortunate that there was full employment on the land, for the agricultural labourer could draw no dole, only sickness benefit. The ten-shillings-a-week old-age pensioners could just get by if they were a married couple and had the two pensions to live on. The solitary pensioner often worked a day or two to pay his rent or if he was unable to do this went on Public Assistance. The village Guardian of the Poor knew the circumstances of the old folk and advised the Guardians Committee how much the Relieving Officer should allow them.

The early Thirties in Ashton should be remembered by the thrift of the working man and the loyalty of his wife, who did everything possible to help family, from taking in washing to picking blackberries for market. Gunner got by by picking sprouts in frost and snow and watering spring-cabbage plants in a September drought from Carrants Brook. Milko, that mystery man of the dairy, milked his cows three years running without bringing them to the village bull to get them in calf. He no longer bought clothes but killed the goat which ran with his Red Rubies, skinned it and made a coat out of goatskin. He was a frightening spectacle for the visitor to meet at night as he walked in down-at-heel boots, torn trousers, goatskin coat, ginger beard and hair which should have been blond but through lack of washing appeared a greasy, sandy colour. He still bemoaned the fact that the continuation of the species seemed remote after his fruitless Cheltenham love affairs. Now his Robinson Crusoe appearance dealt the final blow to any chance of marriage.

Fred Cooper's pub, the Dragon, was almost deserted except on Sunday nights. Sacco still visited there, Sacco, who could have been one of the richest men in the village, often ate a pound of sausages cooked with six eggs, over Cooper's fire, then started drinking the cider till closing time. Flora Lights could no longer pay the rent at Coney Burrows after Amy went as receptionist to a Cheltenham hotel and Lil got married to a cowman from Pershore. Ganger was very irregular in his payments to Flora. The Relieving Officer helped her a bit and she sent begging letters to those villagers she knew had a little money. Sacco worked more regularly until he saved enough to buy an old car, not so old as Milko's late one, the one where empty carbide tins formed the exhaust, but a 1925, ten-horse-power tourer which took him to Cheltenham on Saturdays to sleep in the back bedroom of a pub with Amy. Gunner frowned, Mercy frowned and Emma frowned when they heard of Amy's link up with Sacco again.

'Tis natural,' Sacco told Cyril at the Dragon. 'Amy would stand a regiment of soldiers. Come with me one Saturday, she will do you more good than sweeping the churchyard path and staring at Millie.'

Cyril sniffed, told Fred Cooper to draw Sacco a pint and threatened to tell the Revd Vernon of the goings-on in Cheltenham.

The another blow struck Ashton that year. Ganger Firth was moved from the branch line to the main line between Gloucester and Bristol. He left Flora's to find lodgings in Gloucester. Flora was in sad straits. 'I was brought up as a lady, my father was a groom, it's not right for me to go gilly picking or blackberrying with the village women.' So into Evesham she went on the carrier's lorry and pleaded her cause at the Relieving Officer. They gave her a little to live on and her nephew Lloyd, a telegram boy from Evesham, came to live with her.

'You ought to thank God for your dinner,' she said. 'It's plain but it's good. The doctors says I mustn't touch fat, it's potatoes, cabbage, prunes and custard for me.' At the doctor's Flora was asked, 'Have you told me all, Mrs Lights?'

She replied, 'No Doctor, I don't sleep.'

'Why don't you sleep, Mrs Lights?'

'My nerves, Doctor. I think somebody will come out of the bushes on Coney Burrows and say "Now I've got ya". Then I think how silly I am, God will take care of me and I've got Lloyd. But he's not very big and he sleeps.' Mrs Lights came away with a big bottle of brown medicine but still got behind with her rent.

Now Tiddley Chandler heard of Flora's plight and how she owed rent on Coney Burrows and that Careful Sammy would not let her have any more bread until she paid. On the way back from Mrs Tat Steward's with his washing, he pushed his bike with the easel on the crossbar past Coney Burrows. In his sixty years on earth Tiddley had never looked twice at a woman but on seeing Flora weeping at the gate his heart melted as he remembered Harbour Lights dying for his country.

'In trouble, Mrs Lights?' he said. 'Anything I can do?'

'Trouble, Mr Chandler! I've earned nothing from lodgers since Ganger went. Careful Sammy is going to sue me for bread money, Sacco has got Amy in the family way and here I am on parish relief. Me that was brought up respectable.'

That moment something stirred in Tiddley's heart that had never been touched before. A war-widow of fifty, a good-looker at that. Coney Burrows, a snug cottage under the hill, and his studio cold and damp, the rooms fifteen foot square and he alone to cook the meals.

'Can you help me, Mr Chandler?'

'Call me Tiddley, everyone else does,' he said.

'Call me Flora,' said Mrs Lights over the wicket gate.

'I'm looking for a small cottage, warm for the winter, for bed and breakfast, then I can spend my days as usual up in the studio or out on the bike with my canvasses. Will you put me up, Flora?'

Flora could hardly believe her ears. At last a gentleman to have as a lodger. No common platelayer to live with the daughter of the brickyard. 'Yes, Tiddley. How much will you pay?'

Tiddley propped his bike with the bag of washing against a telephone pole and said, 'Let me see my room. . . . Ah, that will do nicely, but just what will the neighbours say? It certainly is a good arrangement, Flora, I'll come next week. How much do you owe Careful Sammy?'

Flora reached the bill from her corner cupboard, the cupboard where Harbour's medals were the presents he had bought her while he was in the Navy. Tiddley left enough money to cover

Careful Sammy's bill and in no time at all he was installed at Coney Burrows as Flora's lodger. The village folk pulled his leg about living under the same roof as Mrs Lights, banned from the Mothers' Union, but Flora fed him his breakfast, made him a nice bed in the spare room and Tiddley went out in the daytime as he always had done and painted in oils the landscapes of the Vale of Evesham. He had some hung at academies, some he sold; then when Amy was well enough, she brought the baby to see Flora and he painted her portrait sitting on a fallen apple tree with the blossom still rose pink and leaves a rich green. This he did in watercolour – Tiddley thought it more delicate than oils for such a beautiful creature.

Cissie Treadwell, the postmistress, brought on her morning round an important looking envelope to the harness room. Sacco was out patching up some old Cotswold house where the chimney had collapsed. When he returned he found it a Paternity Order citing him as the father of Amy Lights' baby boy. It was all cut and dried and not denied and before Sacco had a chance to finish the chimney he found himself liable for seven shillings and sixpence a week until the boy was fourteen years old. Cyril said in the Dragon that had he accepted Sacco's invitation to Cheltenham, Sacco would have put the blame on him.

Looking across the bar, the mason lit another Woodbine which he held in one hand while eating a faggot dripping grease from his toothless mouth with the other, while his pint of cider stood on the table for him to take an occasional sip.

'Cyril,' he said, 'I have a feeling you are trying to make me believe you are a potential father but the fact remains you have not proved yourself. I would say that you are like the man in the bible – impotent.'

Cyril then said that if Sacco had many seven shillings and sixpences to find he would have less money for the car, less money for the drink. Another thing Cyril had heard from Tiddley was that Flora was going to foster the child so Sacco's money would be going to Coney Burrows.

Sacco had his answer ready. 'You, Cyril, Monkey Brand and Tiddley, all staunch churchmen, spend a lot of time with Flora.

Who does she fancy? If Mrs Pride knew that Monkey Brand was cutting her fire sticks and if Revd Vernon knew that you went up there every night to wind the clock up, there would be trouble. I have heard what is commonly known as trading between a man and a woman called some funny things but, Cyril, never have I heard it called winding the clock up.'

CHAPTER NINETEEN

Not Beyond the Pale

Between the wars when the villagers who had County Council holdings drove their B.S.A. 500s to market with coffin-like boxes instead of sidecars loaded with garden produce, Lofty was one of the old school who relied on the carrier. The box sidecar, as it was known, was often the product of the local wheelwright. It was made just wide enough to hold one hamper and with a roped load was half as roomy as a small lorry. Within the compound of our village (I like to think of it as a compound in those days) folk were accepted in a way difficult to describe. We know that the gossip was rife, that any bit of spicy news oiled the wheels of life, but in the main the carter and his wife, the cowman and the shepherd, didn't envy the four-or-five-acre men who in a good year made more money in a month with asparagus and strawberries than they saw in a twelve-month.

It seemed as if no one was 'beyond the pale'. Sacco played fast and loose, Milko was as dependable as a baby's bottom, Flora, the war-widow who had suffered great losses in her family, was still game when Ganger left. When Cyril, Tiddley and Monkey Brand quarrelled as to who should paper her bedroom and Tiddley, the gentleman lodger bed and breakfasted, paid the rent at Coney Burrows, it gave the Mrs Grundies of the village fuel to keep the inevitable fire of innocent cant going.

Ashton had not reached the stage which was sure to come when religion was a middle-class morality. Mrs Pride alone walked whalebone stiff to church, her powdered face beneath a veil. Lofty and the chapel elders took their five-to-six Sunday climb up the bethel steps in navy suits and wore flat, pancake caps of grey or black if a recent death had struck the family.

The farmers wore tweeds, broad-banded, silver-grey trilbies and Percy, who took the collection, was what one might call a relic of pre-enclosure days, working four days on the farm and two on his holding where he grew strawberries, onions and plums. Percy walked the carpeted aisle in Bedford cord breeches, leathered inside the knees, pigskin buttoned gaiters and brown polished boots. A smart Harris Tweed coat completed his Sunday outfit. Head bowed in front of the rostrum, he looked like a good class bailiff on his way to market as he handed the plate to the preacher.

'May these gifts and our lives be used in thy service, Amen,' Gunner's brother said as he stood at the rail, weather-beaten off the railroad. Then the address. Chapel folk of the laity don't profess to preach sermons. 'What shall it profit a man if he gain the whole world and lose his own soul?' This surely brought comfort to the men with the two-and-eleven pancake hats lying beneath the pew in front. 'In my father's house are many mansions' brought a smile to the cheeks of Gunner, thinking of Frank, gone before.

But the preacher, who for six days carried the pickled sleepers and the rails on the branch line, cropped the hawthorn railway hedges, had a gipsy look about his features, the creosote having permeated his very being and bronzed his face and hands, as he shouted, banging the book, 'What does the poet say? What did the Postle Paul say?'; the fervour of 'All hail the power' as Emma fluted the organ, the clocks on Sacco's stockings as he slid late into the choir, Martha's fancy garters and Mercy's bonnet, gave variety where it could have been, oh, so dull. The slickness of the theatre curtain as it opens and shuts for the encores was nothing compared with George Blizzard's gallant attempts with a bean pole to close the curtains at the preacher's back as the sun glared through the windows blinding the congregation with its rays. George struggled, missed the curtain hooks on the high window, tried again, and Mrs Haven, standing by her botanist husband, new from India, who wore spats like a family doctor, nodded a 'thank you'.

At the church, apart from Mrs Pride who was considered odd, Cyril ushered the farmers, the workers, the widows into the pews much the same as penning sheep at market when the young breeding ewes or the aged rams go in separate pens. It's true that if Millie Bostock had trimmed her hat many more times it would have been a harvest festival of fruit and flowers in itself. Cyril Pumfrey, who counted the labourers' pence and the farmers' and retired Birmingham men's shillings, once lost a bottle of Sacramento used for communion. 'Sacco,' he said after one funeral, 'have you drunk a bottle of Sacramento out of the vestry?'

Sacco eyed Cyril cautiously, not wishing to lose his job of grave digging. 'No Cyril,' he said, 'it stands to reason I don't want that cat lap or NAAFI tea after drinking Cooper's cider or beer from the wood. Use your intelligence, it's more milk for you and Millie on the nest of her settee than a man like me.'

Cyril puffed his pipe over the grave while Sacco started to fill in, then sniffing and throat clearing he walked away with Revd Vernon.

'Forget it, Cyril,' the man of the cloth said. 'We will never replace Sacco. You well remember how he helped the undertaker from a nearby village that winter's night?' Then turning to his brother-in-law, Revd Vernon whispered, 'If ever the relatives had known about that, there would surely have been a court case.'

'I remember it well,' Cyril said to the vicar. 'The undertaker's man was bringing a corpse in his horse and cart one winter's night. He called at a public house Cheltenham way and then made for our village church. The drink confused him or shall we be kinder and say he fell asleep. The horse mounted the grass verge and the shafts went up in the air as the coffin shot backwards, breaking the tail board and the coffin end. The poor chap inside came through and the undertaker with Sacco's help worked through the night hours to make another coffin, all very secret.'

How discreet was the four-hundred-pound-a-year man who preached in the valley church! He knew that Sacco spent his evenings at the Dragon, then in the harness room with Milko where the semi-circular iron fire hole, ornamented round the edges, drew the smoke from the coal fire while Sacco's kettle and saucepan simmered in front. The old horse brasses of Queen Victoria's Jubilee hung on their martingales from cart nails on the pitch pine wall. The ceiling was the colour of a Golden Tankard mangold wurzel but not half so bright, years of sulphury fumes had coated the lime white wash until it was just a yellow cloud under Sacco's paraffin lamp hanging from a broken plough trace, but it was warm – his camp bed more of a shake down than a tucked in, two-foot-six counterpane.

As Amy Lights' baby grew strong on Milko's milk with Flora his grandmother at Coney Burrows, Tiddley suggested that the child should be christened. Flora pondered on this, knowing the Revd Vernon to be a good man but not forgetting that she had herself been banned from the Mothers' Union.

'You must get the devil driven out of him,' Millie Bostock said.

'Then in due time he can be confirmed,' Cyril said.

'What would Harbour have done if he had have lived?' Flora often fingered Harbour's medals, shed a tear when a photograph of him slipped through her hands when she tidied the chest of drawers. Harbour and Gunner were good friends before the war. Gunner came back. Who better could name the child than the preacher, Gunner's brother, who had worked on the railwoad with Ganger Firth? More fitting that the preacher's horny hands should hold Amy's first child on the rostrum at the chapel as Flora and Amy stood in the front row of pitch pine pews than at the church. The naming of the boy Amy left to her mother and to everyone's surprise the preacher named him Mason. Tiddley brought a ham from town and Tat, Mrs Steward, Harry, even Careful Sammy, stood before Gunner's brother at the ceremony. 'If he makes as good a mason as his fayther, Sacco, he ull do,' Stodge said, 'that's apart from that thirst of isun.'

Tiddley invited Cyril, Fred Cooper, Careful Sammy, Tat and Mrs Steward to feast off the ham at Coney Burrows just to do the thing right. Monkey Brand Pride dared not go because Mrs Pride, with Miss Curtiss, declared that the child was not legitimate. Cyril and Tiddley smoked their pipes in the artist's studio while Sacco was discreetly absent.

'Put it this way,' Tiddley said to Cyril, 'Amy's a bonnie girl and if you and I were younger and Amy fell into our arms like an autumn leaf as she did with Sacco, it may have been us paying seven shilling and six pence a week. I'll stand by Mason. I know the set-up, he wasn't got on an army blanket in Hong Kong, but he's of our parish, the parish we love.'

Flora Lights told the tea party how she felt that Mason was a blessing in disguise now her family were gone. 'And, Mother, I'm proud of you,' Amy said, 'for all the months I visited the village, weekends from Cheltenham when we knew that I was in the family way and you told the village I had a tumour. Thank you, Mother, and thank you,' she said to the artist, 'for the lovely spread.'

The Miss Curtisses, the Mrs Prides seemed outnumbered that day and Flora's shadow was none the less when she took on the 'Husbud' as Harry called Mason. 'A love child,' Mrs Steward, the washerwoman, called him.

CHAPTER TWENTY

From the Stable Bench

At Mr Dunn's farm the stable was an extension of the big thatched barn. The step was once a squared block of Cotswold stone, but by 1928 it was worn away, rounded and slicked by the horses' hooves as they slid off the stone sett floor to the yard outside and the drinking trough. Inside the open door was the gear house, not to be confused with Sacco's harness room which adjoined the nag stable. The gear house had rough hewn pegs of ashwood sticking out of its inner walls like clothes hangers. On these pegs, when the horses were in for the night, hung the harness. Boxer, Captain, Prince, Turpin and the rest of the horses all had their separate collars hanging from the pegs, check-lined, damp with sweat, with traces of loose hair of different shades bristling from the linings. The oval, leather-fronted gear stuffed with straw and wool had taken the strain all day long from Farmer Dunn's horses' shoulders at plough, harrow, or in the wagon. The mullens or blinkered bridles hung from the head piece, reins first, with the grass-stained bits hanging below the nose band. Mullens could be changed from horse to horse by adjustment of the chin straps but not so the collars; they were made to fit shoulder sizes. Here hung the fillers or thrillers gears, the harness of the shaft horse. How long this combination of leather and chain had been made in this fashion is hard to ascertain. Shakespeare refers to the filler in *The Merchant of Venice,* for didn't he say of Old Gobbo, 'Thee has't got more hair on thy chin than Dobbin the Fill horse has got on his tail.'

To ungear a filler was a matter of use. Harry the carter could do it in the dark as the horse stood at the manger waiting to be loosed from his daytime wear. First of all undo the buckle on the mullen chin-strap, then holding the leather rein in one hand, the head-piece of the mullen in the other, a slight pull forward and the horse instinctively opens his mouth, shedding the bit, and the mullen is ready to hang on the peg. Next undo the chain at the bottom of the hames and the metre strap which fastens the top to the saddle and lift the pair with tog chains tidily hooked to the iron ring. And how easily the hames hang on the peg by the leather strap which joins the top. As you loosen the girth straps, your horse may turn his head from where you have strapped him by the neck to the manger. He may even give a nip with his bared teeth, but this undone, the tail loosed from the crupper, the breeching strap – that semi-circle of broad leather with dangling short chains at each end – is thrown over the crupper. With the left hand hold the cart saddle, the right hand the crupper, hang the filler's saddle by the loop of the crupper on the peg. It was all so simple when Harry did it and no one knew then that Harry's team would never be replaced, for as sure as the shire horses had taken over completely from the bullock team, so Henry Ford's tractors were multiplying daily in this Vale. The long gears were hung, hames first, then the back band, then the chained spreader (long gears being trace harness). One often wonders why Harry and all the carters before made a sort of breathless puffing noise when they brushed the tide mark of sweat off their horses' shoulders or curry-combed the caked mud from their bellies, then used a wisp of straw to brush their backs. It was all so general – never questioned – but it could all be seen from the stable bench.

In winter the warmth of six horses at the manger and one-eyed Blackbird in the loose box provided an animated central heating system in the low-raftered stable with its four walls of Cotswold stone, random built and lime washed. The contented sound of feeding horses mingled with the tired talk of men while the team pulled lucerne from the high hay rack, a rack of cleft ash bars above the wooden manger. Harry called in Mr Dunn to look at Turpin. 'He's a bin in the orchud a-yutting apples, filled his guts, I reckon,' he said to the farmer, who came that evening in slippered feet and half-laced breeches to the stable where the lantern hung from the broken plough trace. At that moment Turpin lay down on the cobbled floor and groaned and kicked, his leather neck band pulling the chain attached until the wooden chog block reached the ring of the manger.

'Undo the strap, Harry, before he's choked,' Mr Dunn said, and as Harry undid the buckle Turpin rose to his feet and came open-mouthed in pain at the carter and his gaffer.

'Steady now,' Harry spoke to the foremost of his team and Turpin turned and stood in line at the manger.

'Fetch George Blizzard,' Mr Dunn told a ploughboy. 'Tell him to bring the linseed oil and turpentine from the cowshed.'

George came while a little group gathered and sat silently on the stable bench. Harry took Blackbird on a halter to the nag stable near Sacco's room, putting Turpin in the loose box.

'What's the confusion tonight, Harry?' Sacco said, as he fixed his bow-tie and clean collar ready for an evening out.

'Gripes,' was the reply, and Sacco-like came the retort, 'Get Woodwards gripe water.' 'No good a talking to senseless craters like you, Sacco. All you knows about is stones, graves and women.'

Back in the stable George Blizzard put a rope twitch on Turpin's nose and looped it in his mouth. With Mr Dunn on the halter George fastened the twitch to a beam above, making Turpin stand open-mouthed with head raised in the loose box. With a long-necked wine bottle, and Harry holding the hurricane lantern, George poured the drench of half-linseed oil, half-turpentine down Turpin's gullet.

'Kip his yed up a minute,' Harry advised, 'just in case he tries to spew it back.' Turpin swallowed and as he did, it was as if an egg passed down his gullet where his powerful brisket bulged in two mounds of muscle.

'He's hellishly blowed like a tick,' George observed. 'Git your yer up anant his ribs and listen to see whether his belly's a working, Harry.' Harry listened with the air of a doctor sounding a patient's chest with a stethoscope. 'Looking worried, Harry, anybody would think you had just missed a good breakfast,' Sacco announced from the open door.

'Now shut thee rattle and stick to thee motor bikes,' and Harry added on the side to Mr Dunn, 'Not a rumble, full a gas from them apples.'

As the other horses stood, disinterested in Turpin's pain, pulling more lucerne from the rack, farting, sending ammonia smelling urine down the stoned channels into the drain, Turpin once more went down with griping pain and groaned, then up again, biting at the wooden manger.

'Out of the road, you chaps and fellas,' George ordered and he and Harry walked Turpin down the lightless yard outside and, swinging another lantern, tried to keep him moving.

'Yur comes the Shepud going up to the Dragon for his bacca.'

'Oi, what be you chaps doing out along a Turpin? Thur's no need to tell mah – he's blowed. Just look at the skin, tight as wax in front of his hips. As't gin him any medicine?' and out of his cord jacket pocket the shepherd took a packet of sweet nitre. 'That ull make him piss, I'll warrant. Our old chap used to use that.'

Sacco went off to the Dragon. He might just as well because what Harry said was true, 'he was no judge of horses'.

After the sweet nitre, Turpin straddled and little boys tittered while Harry whistled to start the water going. Then with hind legs well apart and his peasle hanging like an elephant's trunk but smaller, the apple-soured urine began to run. Even now the two swellings in front of his hips remained and Mr Dunn fetched a bottle of whisky from the house to try to move the painful gas in Turpin's belly.

'We ull manage, Master,' Harry told Mr Dunn. 'He have passed some water so to speak, well, to put it more plainly, he a pissed.'

'Give him the whisky a drop at a time and don't let him lie down.'

'He'll be as right as ninepence come the morning,' George Blizzard said, 'then Harry can give him a branmash and he ull do the job, number two, in front of these byoys.'

The boys tittered as the moths circled the lantern. 'White Hoss,' Harry said as he studied the label on the whisky, and at that minute the shepherd and Sacco returned from the Dragon.

'Whu, whu, whu, whu!' the shepherd chuckled as he saw the whisky on the bench. 'Master Dunn brought that, no doubt.'

'Too good to give horses,' Sacco said. 'Do us more good, I reckon.'

'Wait a bit,' Harry replied, 'this is my job a work. Take Turpin round the yard agun and George, bring the lanthorn.'

They circled the yard, walked to the front of Dunn's house, saw the last candle go out in his bedroom, then back to the stable. Turpin raised his tail, farting until the whole stable echoed the sound and like a football deflating, his huge belly went back to its normal size. Harry gave him a drink of water and bedded him down in the loose box for the night. 'Now we ull draw the cork,' he said, and taking an enamel tot from his frail, poured out for George and Sacco, the shepherd and himself.

'Twud a bin a shum to have given that whisky to a hoss,' Harry said. ''Sides it's agun the law to give alcohol to dumb animals, unt it George?' George nodded assent. Sacco didn't care much about the law but was ready for his tot every time it came round.

Sometime in the early hours of the morning when the boys had gone home, four men of the village went to their beds, warmed with the spirit from Scotland while Turpin spent a comfortable night in Blackbird's loose box, free from gripes and excused to be one of Harry's team when the gears went on at a quarter to seven in the morning. Farmer Dunn was pleased that his best horse was well again and among the chain and leather of the gear house in a recess in the stone wall lying by the oil can was an empty whisky bottle.

But on other nights as the winter wore on, Harry sat on the bench with maybe George, Sacco, Milko and talked of crops, wages, while the shepherd reminded the corded farm men that 'It was Lloyd George who started the old age pension.' Gunner called, tired from his holding, slackened his boot-laces.

'Rest yer feet,' Harry said, 'put a bit of ship's wool under the tongue of your boots. I find that eases my fit.'

Sacco sat by Milko smoking Woodbines. The mason spruced up to meet his latest conquest – Becky Hampton, a companion help to Millie Bostock. As boys in knee-length short trousers sat with the men whose ancestors had worked the land with the long wooden plough in Cromwell's time, Sacco spoke of the old parishioners he had sat up with at night and in his words 'seen tham over Jordan'. Sacco had a gift for this thing. His likeable, often unexplainable way, acted as an anchor simple folk clung to during their last hours. That twinkle of mischief in his eye was welcomed by the infirm. 'They tell me as Tom Solway, as courted Millie Bostock, is a filling with water and mind tha, when that reaches the 'art it's curtains.' So spoke Harry as he laced a crupper with a raw hide leather thunk, or thong, on to a cart saddle.

'Too much rhubarb wine, I reckons,' George said. 'His fayther I remember had a seazure.'

'Emma, Joe's widda, can't keep nothing down, not even water,' Gunner said. Here the boys who could eat green apples and plums all day long were mystified. 'Can't keep nothing down,' young Jim said.

''Tis like this,' Gunner spoke as if he was on the chapel rostrum, 'thur's a "but" in everybody's life. Take Milko yer. Them Rubies ought to have been milked hours ago, but 'tis Milko's way. Then Sacco chasing women. We ud like to see him in the koyr at chapel agin but that's the way of the world. That "but", it is only three letters but it's so important. If you read the Book' ('Yer it comes,' Harry muttered) 'if you reads the Book you will hear tell of a man named Naoman who was Captain of the King's Hosts, a mighty man in valour, *but* he was a leper. Take our King, a good man, approaching a jubilee but he's middling.'

As the spring came along and Dunn's mangolds were fast going from the bury, it was pleasant to sit on the bench and hear the crunch of the horses' teeth as they pulped the sugar-and-water-filled roots in the manger.

'What's a goin to be planted where the mangold bury was?' George Blizzard said. 'Dost reckon it ud grow some taters?'

'Funny thing you should call that to mind,' Harry said, 'we be gwain to plough it on Monday. Me and him and four horses and Master Dunn says if we had a mind to work it we can plant taters.'

After tea on that cold, dry March evening, George and the shepherd came into the stable just as Harry had given the horses their last skip of bait for the night. The horses' heads turned as the corn bin lid slammed and Jim had fetched some sheep cake from the granary in wheat sacks, kibbled ready to mix with the ground oats. Every sound meant something to the horses. The rattle of chains told them they were about to be geared up for work. When Harry mounted the tallet ladder, shuppick in hand, the horses raised their heads towards the empty rack just waiting for the sweet fodder to fall like manna from heaven.

'Well, Harry, how did the addlum plough – "headland" to the scolards, I myuns?'

'Devilish hard, not a dry hair on my hosses nor on my yud. Clats as big as wagon wheel hubs and there they shines in the east wind just like damn great lumps of polished oak.'

The shepherd pushed a bit more shag into his clay pipe, then lit it and chuckling said, 'If we 'as taters as big as that, that ull do.'

'But how be us a gwain to get it down into some sort of mould?' Harry raised his eyebrows and sat on the lid of the corn bin.

'No, I suppose it yunt very long until Good Friday when we will be planting,' George agreed.

As the evenings lengthened and Harry had scuffed the headland, the three men took wooden beetles or mallets to break the largest lumps of concrete-like clay. From the stable bench it was planned to borrow Dunn's bouting out plough for the planting of the potatoes on Good Friday. The double-shield board plough just pushed the still hard lumps of clay into ridges and the potatoes were planted fourteen inches apart into the furrows.

'We ull cover with scratters,' Harry said. A scratter was a fork turned all four tines at right angles by the blacksmith and forming a strong narrow rake. Harry, George and the shepherd pulled the clats back on to the potatoes in the furrows and just prayed for rain to lax the unyielding clay. The showers of April had no effect on the headland of potatoes. The constant wind dried the moisture. By May rows of spindly potato tops forced themselves through the unkind soil. The shepherd, who had no family coughed, chuckled and was dubious of a harvest. Harry and George were worried. 'Shan't get the seed back,' Harry said. 'Unt a gwain to work my guts out a hacking along the rows, let alone mould um up,' George replied.

About July when Harry came in late with his sweating horses from the hay mower, the shepherd sat on the bench and said, 'I a got the finest taters I ever grown since I come off the Cotswolds.'

Harry raised his eyebrows, George chewed another pull of twist and spat towards the horses' hind quarters.

'A'st tried um then?' Harry said.

'Oi,' the shepherd replied, 'if they was much finer you ud have a job to see un — they be about like marbles.'

Harry, whose family would eat a ton in a year, said, 'It yunt worth putting the fork in, I shall have to buy.' This last remark made him look ashamed, having to admit to his wife that they would be buying taters.

'Well,' the shepherd said, 'on the Cotswold we lived on boiled swedes. Master Dunn got a good piece along the road, fry some with some fat bacon.'

CHAPTER TWENTY-ONE

The 'Lectric

The golden glow on a winter's night as the oil lamps slung chained from the beamed living-room ceilings made a focal point above the white damask tablecloths of our village houses as the villagers had tea. Points of flame from the uneven lamp wicks were a constant worry. Globes or glass funnels from the grocer cost about eightpence and a store of these, wrapped in newspaper, lay in the dresser or chest of drawers in most homes. If the hot globe was not upright on the lamp, it touched the cold side of the funnelled shade above and cracked. By candlelight another globe was fixed, by candlelight the uneven wick was trimmed or levelled up by the point of a pocket knife. Millie Bostock's Aladdin with its mantle flame gave a white light, as white as the electric light. But Millie saw the Electric Supply Company erecting poles by Carrants Brook to supply light and power to towns west of us. Politely the men surveyed the land and got the landowners to sign forms whereby they received a few shillings rent for each pole per year. Milko refused to sign and when the pole was erected in his cow ground he cut chips from it at soil level with his axe until Mr Dunn talked him round, explaining that he couldn't stop progress.

'It's all very well to come across our meddas with the poles and wires just a purpose to supply the 'tired colonels at Cheltenham with 'lectric,' Harry said in the Dragon.

'It udn't be so bad if we could tap it and light our housen,' George Blizzard spluttered over his pint pot. 'We can't all afford damn great engines and dynimoes like as one or two a the gentry have got to light their houses.'

The one foggy morning when the power made noises like frying bacon on the wires, Milko went, late as usual, to milk and found one of his cows electrocuted under a pole. 'Dead as mutton her was,' George Blizzard said, 'and if it had bin one of Master Dunn's, thur ud a bin ell to pay.' The Company compensated Milko promptly and handsomely but the whole thing seemed so unfair.

Millie Bostock canvassed the village collecting names of the folk who wanted the electric supply. Everyone wanted it bar Milko, who said that his paraffin lamp lit the house quite enough for him to read the evening paper. Millie by her persistence persuaded the Company to put in a transformer to reduce the high voltage power to supply the village. Charlie from Beckford was busy wiring houses – lights only – for the big switch on in 1934. Millie's electrician came from town and her house was one of the last to be wired, but fortunately it was finished before the Great Day.

Gunner and Mercy, Tat Steward and his wife had moved into the little group of new council houses. Charlie wired them and the council installed slot meters. 'Four bob a wick we pays,' Tat told George Blizzard, who lived in a tied three-shillings-a-week cottage. 'How much is this yer 'lectric gwain to cost us, Charlie?' he asked the Beckford electrician.

'Well, it's about ninepence a unit and to cover the cost of wiring, you people in the council houses will be getting nine-pennyworth of electricity for each shilling you put in the meter.'

Gunner schemed and Tat found out that the bulbs with forty watts used less than the sixties. 'I got a fifteen watt in the privy,' Gunner boasted. 'Plenty a light to do a job for yourself. Oi, and another in the pantry and by switching um off smartish when you comes out a room I can just manage on a shilling a wick.'

As the men talked outside the standpipe tap as they fetched their drinking water, Sacco appeared on his bike. 'Gunner,' he said, 'I am surprised at you going to chapel and staying there, you and Mercy, Sunday nights and Wednesdays just to save your own electric light.'

Gunner replied, 'It's about time you saw the light and you knows what light I myuns. Thee bisn't beyond redemption.'

THE 'LECTRIC

The changeover was the talk of the village. Tiddley complained because his oil paintings didn't reveal the same trueness to nature as they did lit with the oil lamps. Mr Dunn and Kate missed the warmth of the burning wick, the saucer-shaped, white, china-looking shades caused a sameness to creep into the village houses and cottages. You see Tat, Harry, George, all had their different lamps. The one slung from the ceiling was favoured by families with small children but Millie Bostock and her companion Becky Hampton sipped their tea on winter evenings by the light of a table lamp, its round globe resembling the moon at the full. Then of course the Aladdin lit the front room. Some of the older villagers still went candlelit to bed, turning the 'lectric off at the meter every night.

And so a village went on the mains in 1934 taking little of the power from the overhead cables through its transformer. Soon a few wireless sets were mains sets but Charlie at Beckford still charged the accumulators with his generator powered by a great oil engine. The engine ticked over as it stood horizontal on a slab of concrete with its vaporizer white hot as the oil was pumped in through the intake valve. So the cottagers changed from mutton tallow candles to paraffin and now Harry said, 'We be on the 'lectric.'

CHAPTER TWENTY-TWO

The Jubilee

No sooner had the electric made itself felt in the village than the time drew near when the whole country was preparing for the Silver Jubilee of King George V and Queen Mary. Not since 1897 when Queen Victoria celebrated her sixty years on the throne had a Jubilee occurred.

'Form a committee,' Mr Dunn said. 'Nothing can be done without one.'

'Wait a bit,' Tat Steward reminded him, 'first we wants an hexterordinary Parish Meeting, one called by a few parishioners at a different time to the annual meeting.'

Mr Dunn took the chair at this meeting in the old army hut known as the Recreation Room. Cyril Pumfrey was proposed and seconded secretary. 'Ladies and Gentlemen,' the chairman opened, 'let us do something in this parish fitting to celebrate the Jubilee of May 1935.'

'Fittle and drink, we wants,' Harry said, 'and plenty of it.'

Vicar Vernon smiled as he remarked, 'Harry has a point there, but there must be merrymaking for old and young, particularly the children.'

'Whur be us to hold the sports?' Gunner said. 'It's level in the Wynch and anant the Room.'

The owner of the Wynch agreed but Gunner added, 'I propose that no intoxicating liquor be provided that day and if the Dragon's open them as wants it can go there.'

'Rob a working man of his pint of beer?' Flora jumped off her chair. 'On Jubilee Day?'

Soon pandemonium broke out among the devout chapel folk who were supported by some of the abstainers of the church. Tiddley said, 'I propose no drink is served until after the sports. A man can't run on beer.'

'Our 'usbands beunt pigs like you be insinuating, Tiddley,' spoke up Mrs Steward. 'What bist a gwain to drink the King and Queen's health in — cat lap?' she added, 'Milko's milk?'

Revd Vernon then spoke up, saying that '"Wine maketh merry the heart of man and that when one is old, drink no longer water but take a little wine for the stomach's sake." This is according to my bible.'

When the cheering had died down from the regulars at Fred Cooper's, Joe rose to his feet. '"Wine is a mocker, strong drink is . . . Whosoever is deceived thereby is not wise." That also is in the Book, Vicar.'

Doctor Overthrow, speaking as a medical man, told of the virtues of cider. 'Our ancestors thrived on cider and fat bacon, and now the farmers are using more dusty fertilizers or artificial on their crops, cider clears the lungs from the fine particles and if one of my patients had have drunk cider as he sowed field after field of basic slag, he would have been with us tonight.'

'Surely,' Mr Dunn said as he stood at the trestle table at the meeting, 'surely we are not here tonight to debate the good and evil of strong drink? Let us get this settled though at the onset of our meeting. Those in favour of beer and cider — will someone make a proposition?'

'I would like to propose that with pleasure and would like Gunner to know that the hops, the malt and the red apples of our orchards are sent for a purpose.'

'Hear, hear,' Tat said. 'I'll second that.'

The vote went in favour of Fred Cooper supplying the beer for the Jubilee. Revd Vernon said he was sure his flock would use their discretion and not abuse themselves.

'Thur unt room for all the parish to sit down in the Room,' said Jasper Hill, who remembered two Jubilees before.

Mr Dunn puffed at his pipe, Cyril cleared his throat, Flora Lights nudged Tiddley, then Kate Dunn suggested that the open cartshed near the Room, if cleared of wagons, binders and drills, would accommodate the overspill from the army hut for the meal. 'Pay pickers a shifted in thur since I was a bwoy, the ceiling's black with smoke and no doubt thurs company, we ull be a smothered a flays,' George Blizzard spoke up, 'and besides,' he said, 'Ponto beds down in the one waggon.'

'That can be cleared and if it's your wish the cartshed is at the village's disposal. I suggest Sacco whitewashes it and he is co-opted on the committee.'

Millie Bostock and Becky Hampton agreed to provide tea for the children and after a committee had been formed it was decided that Mrs Steward, Kate Dunn and Mrs Pride should provide the dinner. Mercy and Emma suggested some extra special sandwiches of ham and beef.

'Knife and fork,' shouted Flora.

'Let's consider Mercy's suggestion.' Mr Dunn spoke aside to Cyril but his voice was drowned by Flora, Sacco, Amy, Jasper, Tat, Harry and the rest chanting in unison 'knife and fork'. Miss Curtiss reminded the meeting that meant more table space 'and we have only the Mothers' Union trestles in the Recreation Room.'

'Get some planks, Mr Dunn,' was Jasper's retort. I'll make some long tables in a few nights if Sacco ull help me.'

'Anything to further the cause of their Majesties,' replied Sacco, who had spent half-a-crown at Fred Cooper's before he came, the beer loosening his tongue. As the meeting closed so the villagers knew that the following May the Jubilee would be celebrated in the Wynch.

Jasper sawed his planks, braced them with cross-pieces into rough tables for the cartshed. 'They beunt what you might call refectory, nor antique, but get the trestles under um, they ull carry all the fittle and drink we want.' Meanwhile Sacco was pouring buckets of water into lumps of quick lime and Russian tallow and making a whitewash in a half-hogshead barrel to cover the smoke-stained ceiling, the peapicker-stained walls of the cartshed.

'Always one for his fittle,' Jasper said to Revd Vernon, as Sacco boiled six hens' eggs in the boiling limewash. Revd Vernon, though not chairman of the committee, was an active member and he saw to it that the ladies had some of the best ham and beef ordered from the local butcher and the local bakers agreed to cook it. The trestle tables smelt of new wood, the walls and ceiling of the cartshed had a clean look, a healthy smell, but Ponto's wagon bed looked odd outside by the binder and corn drills. But Ponto had many ports of call and soon found cover in the cider mill at Bumbo. Mr Dunn drove up in his car with a stack of clean tablecloths he bought cheap at Evesham Bon Marché. 'Flora talks of knives and forks, Vicar,' he said. 'Well, you have it announced at church and Gunner will at Chapel, that everybody brings their own utensils.'

There was a mist along Carrant Brook meadows on Jubilee morning as the sun rose over the Cotswolds' hoar-frost-whitened green hedges; nine-inch-high stinging nettles lay flat and frosted that May morning in the brook meadows. 'My eyes, what a reamer,' George Blizzard greeted Gunner as they crossed in the Back Lane, George bringing in the milking cows and Gunner on his way to cut the asparagus. The asparagus buds were still frozen as stiff as pokers by eight o'clock and wanting his work finished early he had arranged with Sacco to help him cut the purple shoots that bristled from the beds like miniature rick pegs. 'It is to be hoped the carrier's lorry ull be yur early and this can be in the market before it's thawed,' Gunner said in an almost despondent tone. The carrier came and the local shops bought the twig-tied hundreds. The merchants could not risk sending such stuff by train, it was a case of into the shops and cooked the same day. 'Frosted grass (asparagus) won't keep,' Gunner remarked as he slid his pronged knife under the buds, cutting at least two inches below the surface to make sure of bleached butts to the buds.

Sacco laughed. 'Summat to laugh at, unt it, to see a frost in May. I was just thinking of Freddy's peas in the Wynch. Early birds in the pod and going black in the sun as I passed on the bike. Your asparagus, Gunner, will be ready to cut again tomorrow after the hot day which looks promising.'

Gunner half agreed and then took Sacco over to see his early strawberries. The white petals with golden centres made a pretty contrast with the green leaves with the wisps of barley straw already laid under the trusses of bloom. As the sun increased in power and the white rime melted on the brookside hedge, so the golden centres of strawberry blossom turned black. 'That's the fust pick killed, Sacco, and as you know the fust wick's strawberries be allus the best price in the market.'

Up in the Wynch meadow adjoining Freddy's peas, Farmer Dunn and his committee were preparing for the Jubilee sports. Men of the land who cared looked wistfully at the peas. Women who were banking on some early pea-pickers were sorry. Sorry for themselves, sorry for Freddy.

'Summat on it,' Harry said, 'when a mon plants his pays in late January, horse hoes um, hand hoes um, kips the crows off um, then this blasted frost.'

Milko, who had been persuaded by Cyril to get a new suit for the Jubilee, arrived early, his cows already milked. An Evesham tailor had made two journeys by train to fit him up in Harris Tweed. 'God bless me, am I seeing things?' Mr Dunn said to Kate as together they were erecting the Aunt Sally. Revd Vernon arrived after coffee with Millie and complimented Milko on his outfit. Fred Cooper brought the beer into the field on Dunn's dray. No sooner was the tap on the barrel than Sacco said he thought he should sample it. 'A drop of good ale, Fred,' Sacco said, smacking his mouth towards the vicar.

'Well, he should know,' said Revd Vernon turning to Cyril.

The women with the donkeys from the hillside village brought the coconut shies and donkeys for the children to ride. Cyril marked out with whitewash the slow bicycle race and the hundred yards flat race for men and women. Two ash poles pegged at two-inch intervals were the uprights for the high jump.

'Five bob prizes for most on it,' Tat Steward said, 'according to the Committee's rules, and Cyril's decision is final as to the winners.'

Whatever Tiddley had said about no drink before the sports,

Fred Cooper had his usual customers having their morning livener already. Mrs Steward, Kate Dunn and Mrs Pride had laid the tables in the Recreation Room the night before and were now laying the long trestle efforts of Jasper in the open cartshed. Villagers brought their own knives and forks and picked their places either in the shed or in the army hut.

'No top table today,' Mr Dunn said. 'We are a united family under King and Queen.' One o'clock was dinner time (or lunch time to some.) Mr Dunn and Revd Vernon carved the hams and the beef. Tat and Harry stood as the slices fell on the great meat dishes from Dunn's kitchen.

'Nice bit a biff,' Harry said to Tat who, clearing his throat, replied, 'Oi, biff allus is meunt to be cooked in a smartish jiunt. You understands my meaning, if it's cooked in almost a quarter like this and gin time in the hoven, the flavour don't escape. Now take our usual Sunday jiunt, it unt big enough to cook avout it shrivelling up like a ball of rubber. I'll tell tha, Harry, we be in for some fettle as won't be forgot for many a day.'

The tables were soon covered with beef, ham and tomatoes, lettuce, onions, pickled walnuts, cheese with trifle and cream to follow. Revd Vernon called Gunner on one side saying, 'Now in the village where every one is loyal to the crown, where the Union Jack flies big or small from every house and even the flowers in the gardens are red, white and blue, it's fitting we say grace before the meal. I can't be in the army hut and the cartshed, so would you say grace in the cartshed, being a highly respected member of the chapel?'

'As you say, Vicar, I shall consider it a honour.'

In the red, white and blue-festooned Recreation Room, Revd Vernon called a hush as he said, 'Be present at our table, Lord. Be here and everywhere adored. These mercies bless and grant that we may feast in paradise with thee.' 'Amen' added Cyril.

In the open cartshed where Sacco's whitewash had covered the smoke-blackened ceiling joists and Jasper's unplaned tables stretched into the far end, the chapel benches either side, Gunner raised his right arm, the palm of his hand downwards in a priestly fashion. 'All eyes closed, friends,' and in the silence he recited in his broad Gloucester-cum-Worcester accent, 'We thank thee Lord for this hower food, but more becos a Jesus blood. Let manna to howr sawls be given, the bread a life sent down from heaven.' 'Amen,' Sacco said, and the knives and forks were soon busy.

When the plates were empty and only the serving women were left in the room and shed, young girls tittered, old men belched as they climbed the stile into the Wynch Meadow. Gunner looked across the iron railings to Freddy's flattened peas. Sacco challenged Milko at Monkey Brand's stand. Here a slippery pole lay horizontal between two sawing horses and each contestant sat astride the pole with a pillow in one hand facing each other. Without holding the pole each pillow fighter tried to knock his opponent off on to the grass below. Sacco, toothless and grinning, swiped at Milko who ducked, sending Sacco reeling to the ground. Then Sacco's pillow hit the target and Milko was dislodged. This simple, old-time rural sport gathered quite a crowd of onlookers. Ganger Firth who visited the village that day was eyed with suspicion by Tiddley. Not that Tiddley shared the same mattress as Flora Lights, but he did live under the same roof at Coney Burrows.

'I'll take you on for half a dollar,' Wisdom Loveridge challenged his old partner of the Dragon. Now neither Firth nor Loveridge had been at the barrel like the previous contestants and they rained blows with the pillows which failed to dislodge either of them.

'Call it a draw,' Monkey Brand Pride shouted after five minutes.

Sacco and Milko throwing at the coconuts were filling the arms of Amy Lights and Becky Hampton with their winnings.

'Will the contestants for the hundred yards men's handicap race line up, please,' came Cyril's voice through the old gramophone horn.

'Fifty-nine I be,' Gunner said to Harry, 'and we went to Ayshon school together. Let's have a go.' At the starting line

Sacco and Milko stripped in the burning sun. They stood with the young men of the village raring to go. Cyril acted as handicapper and put Gunner and Harry twenty yards from the start, while Wisdom and Ganger Firth were a few yards behind them.

'We will do the job properly,' Cyril shouted. 'Mr Dunn is starter and will fire a blank from his twelve-bore when you are to start.'

'I yunt no use a running in heavy boots,' Gunner said to Harry. 'I bin in this caper afore, 'tis better in stockinged fit.'

So Harry and Gunner left their boots in the sides lines where the crowd gathered. Towards Freddy's peas Farmer Dunn fired his twelve-bore gun and the handicap was away. Handicap was the right description as Sacco and Milko tried in vain to overhaul Gunner and Harry. Gunner broke the finishing tape two yards ahead of Harry and Sacco, going like a steam engine, gaining all the way, came in third. As Gunner took the five shillings from Cyril and he and Harry were doubled up breathless at the post, Sacco looked Cyril Pumfrey in the face saying, 'I thought a churchwarden should be a fair-minded honest man, and you a disgrace to the church and their Majesties — gave twenty yards start in a hundred to competitors against Milko and me.' Cyril sniffed, lit his pipe and said, 'Remember what Tiddley said at the meeting — "Men don't run too well after beer".' Sacco's blue eyes looked angry as he answered, 'it will be a long while before I say "Cheers" to you at the Dragon, Cyril.'

But the merriment went on. Charlie from Beckford had rigged up an amplifier which filled the air with music. The children had their teas in the Recreation Room with Millie and Becky. The lath between the pegged ash uprights for the ladies high jump was put low for a start. Amy, Becky, Lil and Wisdom's daughter skipped over it with hitched skirts quite easily. As the pole was raised, only Becky and Amy were left in the final jump off. Sacco kept a wistful eye on Amy's garters as she vaulted the lath. Becky tucked her skirt inside her knickers and the staid men of the land stood dumbfounded, then

George Blizzard fetched the Revd Vernon. 'Now, Vicar,' he said, 'I a sin some sights in my time at Blackpool and the like, but just look what Becky's a showing!' Wiping the sweat from his brow he added, 'It's more than human nature can stand.' Becky won the ladies high jump and chatting to the vicar afterwards heard what George had said. As they came together under the walnut tree in the shade Becky said, 'Another thing, Mr Vernon, Ashton folk, the ladies in particular, disapprove of my low-cut dress.'

'Well, your breasts do show when you run and jump but I have no objection.'

'My boy friends say that when they put their ear against my heart they can hear the Bells of Heaven ring.'

'Indeed,' said Revd Vernon, 'that's odd.'

'You listen,' replied Becky as she pulled the vicar's head between her breasts.

'Yonder!' shouted Gunner to Tat. 'The morals of the village be gwain as it says in the Book, 'tis the last days afore the judgement.'

'Now Sacco, no hard feelings, the men's high jump,' Cyril said to him aside, 'and no handicaps.'

Sacco and Milko glided over the lath as Cyril put it one peg higher. Wisdom, middle-aged but an outdoor man, earned claps from the crowd as he cleared the jump shoulder high.

'It gives me pleasure to present Sacco with the prize of five shillings,' Cyril's voice boomed through the gramophone horn.

As the evening wore on the children tired, the donkeys wore a track where they had walked with their young mounts with Mrs Hawker all day long. A friend of Cyril's then started sending up paper balloons, big and coloured, red, white and blue. These hot air balloons with their wad of methylated spirit-soaked cotton wool rose in the air and without a breath of wind went out of sight. The sports were almost over. The bonfire by the Cuckoo Pen had been built for weeks and was waiting to be lit in the dusk of May. The school piano loaded on Farmer Dunn's dray was waiting in the farmyard to be pulled up Bredon Hill to the Cuckoo Pen by two of Harry's horses. At the bonfire of hawthorn hedge trimmings which two of Dunn's men had cut from Parkers Hill the mixed crowd gathered. It was built on a worn-out farm dray soaked in paraffin. Cyril crawled almost under the bed of the dray and with a stick wrapped in sacking soaked in paraffin he lit the pile.

'Like a straw rick it ull go,' Tat Steward said to George Blizzard.

'Dry hawthorn is bound to burn you,' George replied as he lit his pipe from a burning stick from the fire. Cyril took round torches of sacking-covered nutsticks soaked in paraffin so that the villagers could share in the fun. That is to say the young chaps and the girls. As they circled the Cuckoo Pen, Sacco played the school piano on the dray as never before. The latest jazz didn't come amiss to the cinema-going youth of the parish. They sang and danced in a circle around the fire as the hill folk had done in the Merrie England of Elizabeth the First's time. Then the old men told their tales of the Queen's Jubilee, pointing out to the less informed the fires on Broadway and Cleeve Hill, on Dover's Hill and May Hill by the distant Severn. Vernon told the children that these fires had spread the news good and bad right through history, the approach of the Armada and many other events.

A small barrel of Cooper's ale lay between two pieces of quartering at the back of the dray. Sacco stopped playing, beads of sweat dewed his brow. 'Reverend,' he said, 'a small tot drawn from the wood would not come amiss to your friend Charlie Kunz.' The vicar was puzzled for a brief moment, then he knew that Sacco was our Charlie Kunz and despite the quantity of ale that had slaked his thirst in the heat of the day he was dry again. 'Now how about a solo from his Reverence on this auspicious occasion?' Sacco called to Cyril and the Revd Vernon's deep bass voice echoed around the hill from plateau to plateau. The fireworks streaked from hill to vale, rockets off Broadway sparkled six miles away.

'Britain has something to be thankful for this night,' the vicar said as the fire died down and Sacco played the doxology to the tune 'Old Hundred' followed by 'The King'. Millie met the crowd going down the hill with Becky Hampton.

'Vicar,' she said, 'my wireless forecasts thunder. Will you stay with me at the cottage? Becky will be out until the small hours. A chicken's in the oven and will be ready in half an hour and there's some of your favourite sherry.'

'Under the circumstances, yes,' said the middle-aged bachelor.

'Put this tarpaulin over the piano,' Harry said to George, 'and Cyril and I'll fetch the load down in the morning.'

Back in Dunn's cartshed Cooper's big barrel of beer ran dry. 'It is but twelve o'clock,' Sacco said, 'and you, Vicar, are a man well-versed in the scriptures.'

'Well, Sacco,' he said, 'that is my profession.'

'You recollect the wine running out at Cana in Galilee?'

Vernon, who stood by Millie in the lantern-lit shed, replied, 'Yes and I'm glad you have at least some knowledge of the word.' Gunner spoke up saying that the wine at Cana was fresh from the press and the devil had not entered into it.

'The fact is,' Sacco said, 'some of us want more drink.'

Monkey Brand Pride, his wife in her veil close by him, nervously suggested he had a barrel of cider four years old and untapped in his stable and they were welcome to it. 'Good night to one and all and God bless the parish' was all the vicar said as he walked towards Millie's cottage. In Pride's stable, empty of horses for five years, the barrel was handy in the manger. Landlord Cooper put in a tap and the golden juice was deemed to be good. Boltings of straw were laid on the stone sett floor in a circle. The lantern lit the place. Mugs were handed round as Cooper drew the drink. Sacco sat close to Becky Hampton. 'Milko,' he said, 'I am in grave doubts whether you have emptied the udders of your cows and it's turned midnight.'

'No delivery tonight,' Milko said. The almost unrecognizable midnight milkman was sharing a bolting of straw with Amy Lights.

'Let him alone. Who wants milk on a night like this?' Tat Steward said, feeling Milko might benefit from a break in his unorthodox routine.

'Ah,' Wisdom Loveridge said, 'cows have a different life to our people. They have their tits pulled twice a day and only bulled once a year.'

'This cider's sly,' said Harry. 'Don't let the young uns like the mason and the milkman have too much.'

From his jacket pocket Sacco took a mouth organ, vamping the tunes of the day and yesterday. Harry's mouth dropped open as he snored on the straw. Tat climbed unsteadily into Monkey Brand's manger and was soon 'driving them home'. Amy slid her arm around the smartly tweeded Milko who instinctively slipped his hand under the low-cut dress and softly held her breast. Sacco winked and in the unlit loose box of Pride's stable they were soon doing what comes naturally on the straw. Milko, who had drunk as much that day as his cows gave milk, rolled into the next standing and to bed with Amy on the straw.

'Shall we?' Milko whispered in Amy's ear.

'Go on, let's.' Amy, who, though likeable, had been an adventuress, said, 'Got any of your Dad's sovereigns left, say a couple, I'm broke.'

As Milko drew two Queen Victoria sovereigns from his trouser pocket, Amy made it easy for him to make love in the old-fashioned way. Then a quiet sleep fell over Monkey Brand's stable apart from the snoring of Tat and Harry.

Revd Vernon and Millie ate the cockerel, drank the sherry. He spent the night on Millie's sofa. Thunder and lightning were not in her dreams but dreams of Revd Vernon and Tom Solway of the Fire Brigade.

At four o'clock the next morning, Milko left the stables in a drunken stupor and entered the church. He lay in front of the altar covered by the gold emblazoned altar cloth. His second sleep was deep, a complete unconsciousness of everything around. Convinced in his dream he was in heaven, he was still there under the cloth in the mid morning. Revd Vernon walked into the church and finding the door open was curious. Something unusual under the holy table, he thought, as in his cassock he walked the aisle. Milko twitched, Vernon stood back a pace shouting, 'Who is there?' Milko stood up, flung his arms around the vicar saying, 'Saint Peter, Saint Peter, it's you! Saint Peter, oh be joyous unto the Lord.'

'Steady, Milko! You are in church, not in heaven. You know me,' the Revd Vernon said, trembling himself as much as Milko. 'We all had a happy day yesterday. Milko, hadn't you better get changed and milk your cows.'

'Just one confession,' Milko replied. 'I did ravish Amy in Monkey Brand's stable.' 'Don't let that worry you,' the vicar said soothingly as he put his hand on Milko's blond clean hair. 'Yesterday was the Jubilee, let us all get back to our work or calling. I was proud to see one of the last of Ashton's sons whose family had farmed here six hundred years in a fine cut suit. God bless you, Milko.'

CHAPTER TWENTY-THREE

Fourteen Pilots

Farmer Dunn, a bona fide man of cattle and corn, had grown wheat on Unnberland length, in rotation with roots and clover, since he had farmed that roadside field.

'Why dosn't try a feow early pays on that five acres anant the turnpike road?' Gunner asked him as they met at the harvest festival. 'Plenty a men walks that stretch a road from Asum Grubber to Tewkesbury Workuss. They ull pick um.'

Mr Dunn pondered in his mind the gamble he would be making breaking from the age-old rotation and growing market peas. ''Tis the same corn break as growing 'oss byuns (horse beans),' Gunner said, 'and with all that yard muck you got ploughed in afore armistick day that ull grow pays to be sure.' At length Harry ploughed in the yard muck with a three-horse team, the land being brasky, not heavy clay like the neighbouring Hurness field.

'No doubt it ull be worth a bit off my bill,' Gunner told his Evesham seedsman, 'if I tells ya of a mon, a farmer mind, as contemplates growing pays. Five acres mind, not just a feow quarts a sid.'

The seedsman held his bicycle in one hand and patted Gunner's shoulder with his other, saying, 'On the land around here I would advise Pilots. What do you say, Gunner?' Gunner ran his hands over his bristly face and replied, 'Your Pilot sid last year suited my ground, and early too.'

Mr Dunn's seed came to the station in clean white sacks with red stripes. 'Hundredweights,' said Harry as he loaded them on to the dray, 'that's more sensible than the big sacks as mauls yer guts.'

As the January snow melted and the frost held the furrowed land of Unnberland in straight packed lines of brown earth, with powdery mould blowing in the February wind like desert sand flaking from the furrow slice, Mr Dunn thought of pea planting. He walked those drying furrows crossways with Harry, deciding it would be more sensible to scratch the top three inches of soil with the duck-feet drags than go deeper with the four-horse scuffle. 'The scuffle ull bring the muck on top where we don't want it,' Harry said.

The east wind blew, numbing Harry's hands as he drove his three horses crossways over furrows, pulling the duck-feet drags. The frost had thawed, leaving a tilth that only the forces of nature can produce. Mr Dunn scuffed the soil and knew that down below the earth was wet and cold apart from the yard muck which in years past had grown his horse beans and now would, he hoped, grow his first crop for market: early garden peas.

Harry led the horse while George Blizzard held the two tails of the pea drill. 'Et,' shouted George when he wanted Harry to keep to the right. The Gunner looked over the roadside hedge. 'As't ever held a pay drill afore?' he said to George.

'No, can't say as I ave. And the more I pulls the tails or handles to the left to keep to the wheel marks of the last row, the more the drill goes to the right.'

'Just assid backuds you be, George. It yunt no use a thee pulling the tails that a road. It's a matter of balance. When you wants the drill to come to the left, just bear on the left handle of the drill and you will get a drill mark as straight as a arra. We don't want them Sedgeberrow men to take the rise out of our work this side the parish boundary.'

The peas were planted and harrowed in. The February frost returned; the sun went to bed over Bredon Hill like a ball of fire; but the ground was cold. The good earth stood still.

By March Harry and Mr Dunn with pointed sticks dug for the peas which were chitted and, as Gunner put it, 'They a gone down with thur little roots and be now started uphill.' Apart from the first few rows when Mr Dunn's farm men were learning how to drill peas, the rows were fairly straight. 'Put the flat roll over um, Master Dunn,' Gunner advised, when

Harry could see where to lead the horses between the rows. The pea field now looked clean and tidy in the spring, ready, in fact, for the horse hoeing and hand hoeing to follow. Gunner, feeling a bit responsible, looked at the field almost every day.

Dunn's peas grew like hop wire. 'They be shooting up like poplars,' Harry said in the Dragon.

Sacco, knowing nothing about peas, suggested that the pickers might have to get ladders to pick them. 'Good place for a stroll, Becky,' he said, 'when the toil of day is over and a little relaxation is called for.'

'Yes,' Tat said, 'I know and all Cooper's customers know what you mean by relaxation.'

Sacco stiffened his supple frame. 'Tat, my old friend, it's sad that a bit of love-making is just a pleasant memory with you. But I'm potent and Becky knows it.' Becky blushed as she said, 'I just can't see what all this has got to do with Mr Dunn's peas.'

'Now, Harry, you planted them,' Fred Cooper said. 'Have you overdone the manure? Pilots, Gunner told me, grows a smartish bit of haulm. They beunt in bloom yet.'

The next week, as the sun warmed the earth after Stow Fair, Gunner met Mr Dunn in the street and announced that 'the pays be in hackle.' 'Hackle?' Mr Dunn said, 'I don't understand.' 'Well, in a manner of speaking they be sort of in bud. The blow, or blossom, ull come in a day or two if the sun shines and the nights beunt too cold.'

Excitedly Gunner ran from the turnpike road one May morning up to Dunn's Farm. 'Master Dunn,' he said, ''tis stunning news I have for ya today. The pays be in the full blow.'

'What of it, Gunner?' Mr Dunn said as he leant against the stable door.

'All colours a the rainbow they be. A sight for sore eyes. I bin perticular, mind, and fourteen different varieties of pays be on Unnberland length. But worst of all they be a kind of cattle peas, or fit for racing pigeons.'

'Kate,' Farmer Dunn shouted, 'bring me a mug of my best perry and give Gunner a cup of tea, then we will harness the pony in the trap and go down to Unnberlands.'

Gunner said, 'I be mortal sorry about your misdeal, but in the word it says, "Ye shall know them by their fruits". The pods beunt formed yet but it also says, "Do men gather grapes of thorns or figs of thistles". The sid could not have been Pilots. My seedsman has let you down.'

Down in Unnberland Mr Dunn and Gunner found peas growing as tall as poplars. Peas with white flowers, blue flowers, purple flowers, pink flowers, red flowers and yellow flowers.

But worse than this, Mr Dunn's crop was only a fraction of the Pilots in the Vale. In the villages for miles around peas grew higher than the hedges and flowers competed with the convolvulus and hedge plants. A pretty but sad sight.

The seedsman's 'outright', as he was called, was bombarded with messages from growers – big men and little men. The firm's top experts came from London and soon saw the havoc among the early peas in the Vale.

Before the pods formed the pea haulm was pulled up and taken to London. The flowering vegetation was preserved. Then, when the pods formed, pods no bigger than sweet-peas, samples of those were taken to London.

Things moved very fast towards a High Court case in London. The grower who grew the peas in New Zealand was summoned at once. The market gardeners of the Vale sued the seed merchant for selling a valueless variety. The merchant sued the New Zealand grower for selling them and sending them into the country. Mr Dunn, being a man of business experience, was called as a witness for the prosecution by the merchant. He took with him Gunner, who had grown peas and studied varieties since he was a youth.

That hot summer's day in London when the temperature reached 90 degrees, the judge took off his wig in court. The Bar was festooned with peas in flowers of all colours, with peas with short pods – useless for market. The New Zealander in the witness box declared that the peas did resemble Pilots. The seed was round, not wrinkled, and the seed resembled Pilots.

'Call Mr Dunn.' The words rang through the court. Then Mr Dunn admitted that he had never grown peas before but his neighbour who had accompanied him to London had grown Pilot peas over the other side of his fence for years. 'Where is your neighbour?' And Gunner stepped forward to give evidence.

'How do you recognize a Pilot pea?' A learned barrister, who represented the New Zealand grower, asked him. 'It's use, isn't it?' Gunner said, 'and if you have seen them grow as long as me it's easy to spot them.'

'Do you see any Pilot peas hanging from the Bar?'

'No,' Gunner replied.

'What do you see?'

Gunner was silent for a few seconds, then he exclaimed, 'I see fourteen sorts of peas up there and not one is suitable for sending to market.'

'Will you describe a Pilot pea?' asked the K.C. Out of his pocket Gunner produced some fine pods he had gathered off his land from seed from another source. 'This is the Pilot,' he said. And turning to the British seed firm's Managing Director said, 'Am I right, Sir?'

'I swear that the peas in the witness's hand are Pilots.'

The judge, after days of deliberation, ruled in favour of the seedsman and in favour of the Evesham growers. How much compensation the New Zealander had to pay is forgotten.

Sacco, as ever, had the last word. As Gunner came from chapel he said. 'A lawyer at the bethel tonight. Where's the judge's wig?'

Gunner turned to Sacco. 'I tell tha summat and the truth needs no study. Dost thee remember sowing that sid on Milko's little medda as he ploughed up? You thought it was clover, so did Milko. A clover ley for the cows and it came up a field of parsley. So if I was you, bwoy, I'd keep quiet about the fourteen Pilots if you can't tell parsley sid from clover.'

CHAPTER TWENTY-FOUR

Punting on the Avon

On Sunday afternoon in late spring when the Avon river had the apparently safe appearance, Sacco hired a punt, and with a clean white shirt and silver grey Oxford bags, looked the part as he poled the river bed.

Milko, cleaned up, went with him on the rare occasions when Sacco was short of a bird to spoon with under the withies. 'Bring the catapult Sunday,' Sacco told his friend in the Dragon, 'you never know what there will be to have a pot shot at on the river bank.'

As the two paid their hire for the boat, Sacco stood full height at the rear end of the punt, just dabbling the pole in the water in the shallows near the boat house. 'Hope you can both swim,' the boat owner said. ''Tis seventeen foot dip down by Hampton Ferry.' Milko sat in the hull with his catapult and lead shot moulded in clay in his Norfolk jacket pockets.

'Away she goes,' Sacco shouted — a shout that echoed through the open ends of the Bell Tower. Now when Sacco used a punt pole he used it like everything else he used, that was to the limit of his power. Every time the pole found the river bed, Sacco leant all his weight so that the punt shot forward like a rocket.

'Where is the seventeen feet?' Milko meekly asked, 'cos jest be careful mind, we don't want to make news for the *Evesham Journal*. There are quite enough inquests in there.' Sacco puffed at his cigarette and with a wink said, 'Milko, don't say that you are nervous with me at the helm. I can swim half a mile and put you on the bank.'

The punt pole in Sacco's hands worked like clockwork. The smooth speed of the punt as it parted the water lilies, the whistles from Sacco at the courting couples under the withies, showed once again the sheer freedom, the abandonment of the mason as he enjoyed his Sunday on the snaking Avon.

'Not too near the bank,' Milko shouted as they ducked under an overhanging willow tree.

'Bet ya half-a-crown that you can't hit that moorhen,' Sacco said to the catapult man.

Milko, taking up the challenge, took his catapult from his pocket and selected a nice round shot like a ball bearing. The moorhen was perched on what appeared to be some flotsam and jetsam gathered against a swampy patch near Glover's Island. 'Easy,' Milko said, as the eleastic of his weapon was stretched to its full length and his fingers gripped the forked stick in one hand, the leather pad in the other. Ping went the lead and missed the bird but glanced off some round, hard object, taking with it what appeared to be brown pond weed.

Ping went the lead again, and again the shot missed as the moorhen flew away. This time Sacco poled the punt nearer to the target. 'My God,' he said, 'it's a body, a female caught by her belt on a withy bough.' 'What shall us do?' Milko looked scared.

'Now I know what you are thinking my old friend, and if you think that the lead from your catty has any bearing on the death of her you are altogether wrong. She has been in the water for weeks. You see, Milko, if you have smelled death as often as I have you would know.' Milko relaxed as Sacco steered the punt to the river bank. 'Stay where you are,' Sacco said, 'and I'll fetch the police.' Soon he returned with the village constable.

'Ah,' the policeman said as he wiped the sleep from his Sunday afternoon eyes, 'Mrs X. She has been missing now for about a month. That's her, no doubt.'

Sacco said, 'How can we get her to the bank, or do you want to?'

The policeman said, 'It's just my luck to have her on my beat on a Sunday afternoon. She is getting a bit high, but she will have to come out.'

'What's it worth to send her down stream? I mean accidentally release her belt and she could go down to the lock.'

The policeman said, 'Under my order you crafty mason, you push with the punt pole and try to release her. If she goes down stream, and there's a fair current just here, she'll be out of my beat.'

Sacco heaved and shoved the water-logged body until it came adrift and with half-a-crown in his pocket from the policeman, Sacco and Milko followed the drowned woman in their punt as she went with the stream towards the lock. Up against the lock gates she floated as the water swirled past her. The lock keeper, informed, fetched a policeman from another village to recover the body. Sacco tied a noose in a rope and he and Milko helped the policeman to haul the body on to the bank. 'Four hundredweight I reckon she is,' Sacco told the constable. The Woodbines sent up clouds of smoke as the three men waited for the water to leave the body. 'I don't mind the smell of a dead cow,' Milko said, 'but humans, that's different.' As the policeman fetched a large sack a gipsy arrived on the river bank complete with earrings, clay pipe and red muffler. 'Got a corpus theur, maister?' he said to Sacco. 'Not one of our people. She's dressed like a moneyed lady. Cor, look at the diamonts on her fingers. You find me honest, maister, but had that been a man with a gold watch, that could have got lost in the water.'

The policeman brought the sack. He was on the point of heaving up his Sunday dinner when the gipsy said, 'I'll sew her up, guvnor, if you won't move our people from the withy beds or our horses off Glover's Island.' The constable nodded. The body was in the bag and the gipsy fetched his horse and waggon to take it to the mortuary.

As the little boys ran behind the Sacco and Milko sat on the waggon, they caught the smell of the four-week old body and they dropped out one by one leaving a bilious trail along the river and grass verge. And so Sacco and Milko, helped by the gipsy and the village constable, delivered one dead body that Sunday afternoon at Evesham mortuary.

Punting back to the boat house without a word, half-a-crown was a luxury for the men to slake their thirst at the pubs before their cycle ride to Ashton.

Oh, the woman. She was on a visit from London and the coroner did have a little piece in the *Evesham Journal*, 'Mrs X from London found drowned at the lock gates.' Sacco and Milko knew that she took her last swim from the withies by Glover's Island. Village constables don't relish these incidents on Sunday afternoons.

CHAPTER TWENTY-FIVE

Careful Sammy's Conquest

As he grew older and had no children, Sammy gave up his bakehouse and took a little holding up Bredon Hill, a stone house and buildings with ample water to drive the water wheel for his chaff cutter. Sammy, who had been a widower for many years, took Emma, Joe's widow, as his housekeeper.

Here he kept some livestock, reared a few calves, lambed a few ewes and his horse and baker's dray was ample to use on his few acres.

'You've slipped up agin,' Sacco taunted Cyril in the Dragon. 'I have an idea that the church bells will be ringing for the couple shortly.' Cyril gripped the silver band of his pipe and gave a few short puffs of the lit tobacco. As he pulled to keep it alight his cheeks lost their bulge. The pipe gave a whistling sound until the contents of the bowl glowed once more.

'What do you mean, slipped up?' Cyril almost growled.

'Well, in a manner of speaking, Emma has been wanting a man for years. She is a good worker in the house and on the land. Why didn't you hang that expensive trilby hat up to her? Sammy will pop the question.'

'What Sammy does is no concern of mine. Besides, he's been married before.'

'I think it was Shakespeare who put the matter in a nutshell. . . .'

'Hells bells, if Sacco unt a gwain to quote words from the Stratford mon,' Tat Steward said. 'Wur was't thee eddecated Sacco? Was it Heton or Arrow?'

Sacco went on, 'My mug's empty. Is there any of my friends who would care to help me drink deeper of the Cotswold barley and the Herefordshire hops?'

'A pint for Sacco,' Wisdom said. 'Let's hear his logic.'

Sacco straightened his bow tie, cleared his throat, then said, 'Ah Shakespeare. Now he said that farmers always puts a ram twelve months old with an old ewe and vice versa, an old ram with a young ewe. That's correct, isn't it, Harry?'

Harry said, 'Well, let Sacco venture into Shakespeare, but I do know that you allus reckons to couple age and experience with the young and unlearned. But what that's got to do with Cyril I just don't know.'

Sacco winked at Tat as he said, 'My education was neither Eton nor Harrow, but I'm high bred and deep learned.'

'I know thee bist,' Harry took this up in a flash. 'Thee wasn't bred up in a crow's nest and learned down a well.'

Sacco, ignoring this, then explained that Cyril, the man who had never had a love life, would be a good mate for Emma who had been married to Joe for some years. All this pub talk didn't alter the fact that careful Sammy Hicks had engaged Emma as his housekeeper up at the Knap.

Emma was stauch chapel still and Sammy drove his horse and trap, the Sunday outfit, to a nearby church. ''Cos a the Popery,' Gunner said.

Emma, at forty-one, had lived in her cottage and kept the garden planted since Joe died. She moved her few things that spring morning up the hill to the Knap. Sammy stocked the larder well. He liked his food and soon the cows he bought were suckling calves. The hens were laying or sitting on eggs marked with a pencil cross in the rickyard. 'Nice up yer Sammy,' Emma said. 'I yeard the cuckoo this morning.'

The ewes lambed. Sammy, breeched and black-gaitered, drove his trap to market. Emma made a bit of butter and helped him with the calves.

Harry, Mr Dunn's carter, went up Sunday mornings and gave Sammy a hand. He told him the rights and wrongs of sheep and cattle. He was the first one to notice ringworms on one of the calves. 'Give um some linsid cake, that ull help to stop that,' he said. 'Why dosn't join us down at the Dragon some nights? Sacco torments the life out a Cyril down at the beer house.'

The following week Sacco noticed a red patch of inflammation on Sammy's arm just below where his shirt sleeve was rolled. This was Sammy's first visit to the Dragon. 'What dosn't reckon it can be?' Tat Steward said. 'Thee have a look, Harry. As't ever sin anything of the kind afore?' Harry looked as Sammy's arm and instantly recognized it as a ringworm.

'As't got any ink, Fred?' he asked the landlord, "cos bring me some black.' With a wad of cotton wool Harry painted the ringworm with ink.

It was rather late because more had started to itch on his bare arms and in a few days he was smothered. 'How's the lie by?' Sacco asked him one night.

Cyril sniffed. 'Sacco, haven't you any sense of propriety? Just because Sammy has a housekeeper you are insinuating that they sleep together.'

Sacco's toothless gums gripped the lip of the pewter pot as the brown ale ran down his throat causing his Adam's apple to go up and down like the plunger on a roadside pump.

Sammy returned to the Knap where Emma fed the livestock and was fascinated by the water wheel when the sluice was opened and the barn machinery cut the chaff and pulped the swedes. Emma was a farmer's wife.

Sammy Hicks liked a drop of good cider and he even tempted Emma to take a little at bedtime.

The ringworms spread from Sammy's arms to his neck and became very troublesome. He lay awake at night longing to hear the birds sing their dawn chorus in the brake nearby. For hours he tossed and turned with the irritation.

Then one morning he got up at two o'clock and walked in the night air. Walked in his night-shirt for the cool breeze to ease his discomfort. He listened to the cry of the vixen, the hoot of the owls and the grunt of the badgers in the brake. The whistling plovers made their nightly trip as they winged across the hill. Back in the kitchen Emma sat, night-gowned and worried.

'Where have you been Sammy? You ull ketch yer death a cold.'

'I be cold Emma, and devilish uncomfortable.'

They mounted the stairs together. Sammy turned into the housekeeper's bedroom. 'Lors, you mustn't come in yer,' Emma shook as she spoke. 'It yunt decent Sammy.'

'Just one night. I feels middling Emma.' The candle made patterns of light on the flowered wallpaper as Sammy and Emma lay on the bed of duck's feathers. They sunk in the down and lay listening to the murmur of the trees in the brake. 'Damn it, you ull get my ringworms,' Sammy said. Emma never spoke except to say she hoped he would soon be better.

Next night Sammy, at bedtime, told Emma that he did sleep better when she was near. So the one candle was enough to light the couple up the staircase. Emma caught the ringworm, but was careful to conceal this from the village folk.

The lambs were fit for market in September, the chicks had grown to useful pullets and Christmas cockerels when Emma went to the village shop. Sacco was there. 'I do believe you are putting on weight. No doubt being Sammy's housekeeper suits you, Emma.' Emma blushed and walked back up the hill.

That night at the Dragon Cyril was disgusted when Sacco asked Sammy quite openly if a happy event was expected. Sammy took it in good part as he explained to the customers at Cooper's how he never dreamt it was so easy to start a youngster.

'You drive me to Evesham to be a witness?' Sammy asked Sacco.

'I should think so,' muttered Cyril, 'after all his cheek.'

The horse was harnessed in the Sunday trap for the occasion as Sacco drove the pair to the Registrar. A meal at the King's Head and then on the way home Sammy called and engaged the nurse for the day the child was expected.

CHAPTER TWENTY-SIX

High Days and Holidays

In the early Thirties when the workers on the land had no paid holidays except Christmas Day and Good Friday, the villagers who ventured to the seaside were few and far between. Jim, Dunn's under carter, who started at nine shillings a week, had sixpence pocket money. He made a point of asking Mr Dunn to include at least one sixpence in his wage packet. How did Jim budget his weekly pocket money? First of all he had a sit-up-and-beg lady's bike, reconditioned by Sacco. This took him to Evesham on Sunday afternoons. It was threepence to hire a punt on the Avon, twopence to buy five Woodbines, which left Jim with enough to buy a pennyworth of chips. Sometimes he did have a little overtime money, but that was Jim's weekly break from work.

The little crocodile of country folk who dared to break the Sabbath and take advantage of the four shillings half-day trip to Weston-super-Mare could be seen walking with carrier bags of sandwiches, bottles of tea, down the Groaten to the railway station. When one thinks of poverty in the country, it's natural to think of the last century, but the scheming and scraping of our villagers of forty years ago must not be forgotten – it must be admired.

It's true there were compensations for the thirty shillings-a-week man – his cheap house, his potatoes, land and garden, fruit, rabbits and so on – but hard cash was scarce and the Friday night's packet was divided on the kitchen table like a packet of sweets to a family of children. Harry, George, Tat and the rest had always taken this state of affairs for granted.

To see Harry and George and their families walking the country lanes on summer Sunday evenings, or Emma and Mercy blackberrying on the Hill, the children gathering dandelions for their tame rabbits, was a portion of life in the country of the Thirties not easily forgotten.

When Gunner organized the Sunday School outing from the chapel, the collection from the Anniversary Service paid for the children to go to Weston or Malvern by train. Parents who had saved a bit of overtime money made it a day out. Milko came with Sacco to Weston and once never saw the sea, spending the whole day in a pub. Tea on the Grand Pier was a never-to-be-forgotten luxury. Then Gunner with pancake cap, his best dark tweed suit with trousers rolled up to the knee, his heavy boots slung with their leather laces across his shoulders, paddled in the muddy sea.

'I beunt like the Reverend,' he said. 'Beunt afraid to get me fit wet. They tells me as t'other wick he paddled in them new fangled Wellington boots, sniffing the breeze from the incoming tide.'

Gunner told Harry, 'Doctors reckons the hare here is mortal good for the chest and the mud is full a hozone, a regular tonic. This yur salt water ull ease my rheumatics.'

A day at the seaside soon passes. Sacco, except on the occasion of his pub crawl with Milko, posed on the beach like another Captain Webb about to swim the Channel. What stroke he actually did to the delight of the children is difficult to described but he soon tired, and floating on his back reminded George Blizzard of a sheep cast unable to get on his feet. After sending rude postcards to Amy and Becky, Sacco and Milko glared into the penny-in-the-slot machines to see 'What the Butler Saw'. Gunner told them he had got no time for filth 'and they ought to be ashamed of themselves.'

Visits to Malvern with tea at Dorothy's cafe meant changing trains at Ashchurch and then on to the old Malvern line. The blind man played his melodion at St Anne's Well. The cooling spring water was drunk from cupped hands by the Sunday School boys. While the young people reached the summit and viewed the pastoral counties of the middle west, their elders dozed on the seats a little way above the town, looking forward to Dorothy's cafe. Roadmen, for reasons we never knew, always had a shilling or so above the agricultural rate. They even had a day's holiday with pay at times. Before the county councils made themselves responsible for all the roads, the village roads and byroads were under the care of the Rural District Council. Evesham Rural District Council, being a neighbouring authority to Pershore, organized a 'Roadmen's Outing'. The destination was Southend. So picks and shovels and brooms and bagging hooks were put aside for a day at the sea. The Great Western train left early from Pershore and Evesham stations en route for London.

''Tis a Hexcursion,' Stodge told his Elmley neighbour as they discussed it over the parish boundary and the district boundary.

'That myuns,' said Stodge, 'her ull run through London avount hindrance.'

'But some says we shall have to go on the underground across London.'

'Oi,' said Spider Beezely, 'and thee and me be most moderate drinkers, we ull keep anant one another all day.'

'If thee had'st a mind to pay, Sacco, you can come along a we.'

Sacco straightened his tie in Cooper's bar and replied, 'I will come on the train but you cannot expect a young potent man to remain all day with the shovellers of horse manure and the men who scythe the grass verges. No doubt I'll have the pleasure of an attractive female in London or at the sea. Thank you, Stodge, for the offer, but I shall not be staying with the bread and cheese and cider boys that day.'

''Ell of an h'opinion of himself he a got,' Spider said. 'What chance does he think he a got alongside the chaps from the Heast Coast?'

'Now, Sacco, be honest, where the nation hast thee bin?'

'No good trying to explain to men who never meet any company but gipsies, outrights and mile stone inspectors,

Fred,' Sacco said as he walked from the pub to meet Becky under Milko's early pear tree.

The day trip was well patronized by the roadmen of the villages. They looked somehow out of place on the London train. Their tweed jackets, flannel trousers, cord waistcoats and their caps and straw hats were quite enough to convince the business man, Mr Pope, a London friend of the road surveyor who thought it might be an experience to have a day out with the village roadmen of the Vale, of the kind of trip it was going to be. The surveyor wouldn't give a man a job unless the skin on the palm of his hands was hard and gnarled with work. Mr Pope told Spider, 'Nor if he wears a collar and tie. It must be a muffler in winter and a collarless shirt in summer. We beunt what they call white-collared workers.'

The farming on the Cotswolds after the train had emerged from Mickleton tunnel was soon under criticism. 'Our old chap remembers Mickleton tunnel being cut by the navvies from South Wales and the Black Country,' Spider said as Mr Pope picked up his morning paper again. 'Oi, that's what put the tin hat on Dover's Hill Games in the Fifties,' he added, 'games as was set aside at Whitsun for the farming chaps was spiled by the hooligans who worked making the railroad.'

Stodge lit his clay pipe charged with Red Bell tobacco and after a couple of puffs said, 'Square yuds, Master.' Mr Pope was intrigued, puzzled by this. Then Stodge said, 'Wheat on the left. We allus growed that variety when I drove the steam tackle afore I went on for the Council.'

The keep looked better in the meadows by Moreton Station and Spider said the cattle looked kind of slick – 'well ribbed', he said. Stodge looked in vain from the G.W.R. carriage window for Cotswold sheep at Kingham. 'They be must all speckled-faced uns from Wales now a day. The lambs be by a Suffolk.'

'You men I must say have a good knowledge of crops and stock,' said Mr Pope, who came from London.

"Tis like this yer, sir,' Stodge said, 'we a worked the land most of our life and being handy with the bagging hook and pickthank — that's the wooden hook that we use with it for grass cutting — and able to swing the dismal,' ('that's the scythe' Spider butted in) 'the Council be glad of us to keep the village roads tidy. Today,' Stodge said, 'we are off to have a look at the sea at Southend and try the beer.' The biscuit factory, the seed trial grounds at Reading were not passed unnoticed but London was getting near and a cup of coffee went down well with the packed sandwiches.

'It don't seem hardly jossunck (fair) that we be sat here a prying into folk's back gardens — their washing, their hovels and washhouses — when no doubt the front of their houses be tidy,' Stodge told the man from London. He put down his newspaper and said, 'It is a fact you see the worst of a town's property from the railway, you see railway lines don't run along the front of the houses.'

The roadmen's foreman told his men at Paddington that they had twenty minutes to get a drink before travelling on to Southend. Stodge and Spider kept together, dodging the luggage trucks on the platform. Sacco walked sprightly by carrying a folded newspaper, smoking a cigarette in a tortoise-shell holder. He was dressed in a navy blazer, grey Oxford bags, and passed the others as if he did not want to be classed with them.

'Stuck up blighter,' Spider said. 'Dare say when he gets hwome he won't have two halfpennies to rub together.'

Grabbing the handrail, Stodge and Spider went dubiously down the escalator to the underground train. 'I did think the train went straight to the sea,' said Stodge, but the foreman shepherded the men deep under London to cross the city to the east. 'Shan't see Buckingham Palace from here,' Stodge said. Once they saw the light of day again they soon arrived at Southend station.

The roadmen sprinkled the various eating houses and pubs of this London-by-the-sea. 'Funny,' Stodge said as they sat in one pub, 'How the barmaid called me "lovey" and the chap next to me, who I didn't know from Adam, said, "'Ave ya cor a lite, mait".' After walking the shingle, viewing the pier, eating cockles off the stalls, fish and chips swilled with vinegar, and drinking beer, Stodge and Spider sat on the sunny beach, their caps pulled over their eyes and slept the afternoon away.

'Be I seeing things?' Stodge said as he woke Spider. Along the promenade walked Sacco with a blonde woman. 'Skirts up round her ass and plastered with paint − matches the pier I reckon,' Spider said. 'Her's one of them and her ull have every penny off him.'

The journey home from Southend started without incident. All were counted on the train except Sacco and as he was not a roadman, the foreman didn't feel responsible if he chose to stay the night. At London, when the party came up from the depths of the tube to see Piccadilly and were allowed two hours to see the sights, roadmen went in all directions. Stodge and Spider kept together. 'We wants to ketch the train to Evesham and be there on time.'

Two from Pershore had similar intentions but somehow got apart in Oxford Street. Percy Bullock and Marty Smith knew every road, footpath and bridle path around Pershore and Bredon Hill. They knew the drains that blocked in the winter's flood and had often walked together the parapet along the river wall of old Pershore Bridge when the Avon swirled under the arches and over the road on its way to Tewkesbury and the Severn. In Oxford Street Marty slipped into a shop to get more tobacco to recharge his smelly pipe.

'Don't thee gu away, Perce, 'cos this yer place is as uzzy to get lost in as the Sahara Desert. A lot of the roads a got WC wrote on um, no shortage of privies around yer.'

Percy Bullock was soon looking in a fruiter's shop and seeing Huxley Giant strawberries marked up as Royal Sovereign he argued with the shopkeeper, telling him in his own words, 'We comes down yer from Persha where the plums come from. Them Huxleys of thine got no more taste than a marra, thee bist deceiving the public.'

'Covent Garden sent them as Sovereigns and they should know,' the shopkeeper said with interest.

Percy thumbed his leather belt and drew himself up to his five foot seven. 'We grows the damn things and should know,' he said as he walked off in disgust.

'Whur the ells Perce Bullock?' Marty said as he was jostled by rush-hour shoppers. 'Talking to some counter jumper most likely.' Marty was right. A quarter of an hour passed and no sign of Percy Bullock. Then a policeman came up and Marty touching the navy trousers of the arm of the law with his walking stick spoke up, 'Have you seen Percy Bullock around yer?' The policeman looked puzzled and said, 'What's he like?'

'He's a shortish stiff man, about five foot seven. He's wearing a brown tweed jacket, grey flannel trousers, a grey cap and carrying a walking stick, one made of ash like mine.'

The policeman looked at Marty with a certain amount of pity, then said, 'Now look here, there are hundreds of thousands of people just around this shopping area, I can't possibly tell you whether I've seen your friend Percy Bullock.'

Marty puffed at his pipe, cocked his cap in disgust saying, 'Oi, you London bobbies thinks you be clever, got to be six foot and all that, and you can't help me find Master Bullock. Now where I comes from – Persha in Worcestershire – thur's one hinspector, a seargeant and about five bobbies and they knows everyone in Persha. What dost think a that? Whur's the Super?' The policeman made no reply but walked on.

At the appointed time Spider and Stodge boarded the train for Evesham with just a sprinkling of the men who started on the trip. The foreman counted and recounted the men and was worried about the ones left behind. Sacco in Southend was left to his own devices; it didn't matter about him. Late that memorable night phones were ringing in the Vale villages from the men who had missed the connection. At such a late hour no more trains were running to Evesham and Pershore. Percy and Marty at last met on the platform at Paddington hours after their train had gone. 'See them taxi men out there?' Marty said. 'We'd better get one to take us hwome. In any case I shall have tongue pie from the missus cos it's now twelve o'clock.'

'Ull ya take us to Persha?' Percy ventured to ask the uniformed driver.

'Blimey, what a question! Is it norfe or soufe?'

'Now I hopes as you knows a bit more than that bobby in Oxford Street. Don't tell me you ha never eard a Persha, by 'Ooster,' Marty said.

'Mean Woosta?' the taximan said. 'That will cost you a quid or two.'

'Don't you bother yer yud about that, we be well breeched, beunt us, Perce?'

'Jump in then,' and the two men of the road saw the lights of London as the taxi's radiator pointed towards the West and the Midlands. The streets were still crowded as men and women folk were leaving the clubs and theatres. 'Quite an hexperience,' Marty said and sliding the window between them and the driver's seat they asked him, 'What time do these townees get to bed — or perhaps they ain't got no beds?' The summer's night or early morning was quiet in the country and as the taxi came down Broadway Hill, the dawn was just coming up behind them. In the village where they lived just outside Pershore the row of council houses were quiet as the brakes were applied outside Number 10. The taximan said to Marty, 'You live at Number 10 then, like the Prime Minister?'

'Oi, and I lives at Number 11 like the Chancellor of the Exchequer. Does that mean I got to pay the fare?'

'All the same to me, Guvnor. Is that the cuckoo I can hear in the wood opposite?'

'I be dalled if it unt,' Percy said to the driver. 'That ull be about the last time this year, it's Persha Fair time.'

'Like a feow flowers to take back to the mussus?' and with this Marty picked some of his dew-drenched sweet peas. 'The nosey varmints' Percy shouted as the neighbours' bedroom curtains were drawn and windows half opened. 'Oi we missed the train, put that in the paper,' and with a punnet of Percy Bullock's strawberries the taxi turned back for London in the late June dawn.

That Sunday in the Vale the men who worked on our village roads were arriving home in all sorts of ways. Percy and Marty were just two instances. Some got the Cheltenham train and walked eleven to sixteen miles home, arriving about Sunday dinner time. Another party noticed a lorry with Worcester marked on it and came from London that way. Penny numbers would be the hackneyed phrase as to how the Evesham and Pershore roadmen came home from their outing. No, the details of the outing never got in the paper and it was a sore point with the local roadmen for years. But alas, many of them are gone now; the village road man is a rarity.

In the Thirties when men got fed up with work, home life or the neighbours, there had to be some sort of escape – an unwinding if you like. Wisdom Loveridge, a great follower of football, local and professional, got excited when his favourite first division team were in the Cup Final. At half-time on his wireless set he heard how they were 3–2 down. It stayed that way and Wisdom, who had a few bets, lost a little money, but more than that his arguments that his team would win, as he 'conflabbed' with Sacco in the Dragon, touched his pride. He had two weeks on the drink and was never sober from morning till night. These unofficial holidays were spasmodic, unheralded. When Tat Steward fell out with his wife he took to the road for ten days, lying rough as it was known, among the peapickers, drinking his earnings. When he arrived home, the first thing he did was to give his pig ten buckets full of pig wash or swill, one for every day he had been away. Of course Mrs Steward had fed the pig during his absence but she refused to get any food for Tat the first day of his return.

'If we beunt a gwain to yut, we shan't want the privvy up the garden. No closet bucket emptying for me.' So with a hammer and some six-inch nails, he nailed the closet door to the lintel and to the door posts and returned to the house. This ten days away of Tat's can hardly be described as a holiday. Shall we call them highdays?

CHAPTER TWENTY-SEVEN

The Old Rugged Cross

In our neighbouring village where Stodge slept under the thatch in the White City as it was called – a green with just a group of black and white houses built around it, Sacco had been working for years. A Georgian mansion in a bad state of repair had been bought by a Birmingham business man and was being restored. It stood in parkland and was approached by a private road with a lodge where the council road began. Although the mansion was truly Georgian, there were arches and pillars around the garden that had a look of Roman work. These had been added by some previous owner and did at least add richness and grace to the gardens; so did the cedars of Lebanon in the park. Sacco was head mason of the team of selected men who tooled the stone work. Mr Bert Harvey, who had made a packet out of cheap jewellery in Birmingham, came down to the hall in his Rolls Royce when he had time. Bert trusted Sacco and relied on his sound judgment to supervize the restoration.

'If you want the stone work in the gardens Gothic, you can have it Gothic,' Sacco said as Mr Harvey drove him home one night to the harness room. Women, children and the farm men looked and looked again down the village street as Sacco sat erect in the front seat of the Rolls.

'Who the 'ell's he got in with now?' Tat Steward said to Monkey Brand.

On summer nights, instead of cycling three miles to his room, Sacco whiled away the time with Becky Hampton in the thatched summer house near the lodge in the hall grounds. Sacco fried sausages over a devil (a fire in a holed bucket) for supper. Plenty of Fred Cooper's beer and cider, and here Sacco lay all night with Becky, lay in the summer-house when all the other men were gone home. 'It is not good for man to live alone,' he quoted Parson Vernon.

The work was almost completed at the hall. A new staircase had been built by a Pershore craftsman, a staircase wide enough to drive a carriage and pair up. 'If you want quality,' Sacco told Mr Harvey, 'I'll pick your men. I know some of the finest plasterers in the four shires. They will make you cornices and restore the ceilings just as they were when Lady Haslett had the house built and the bell cast that still hangs silent in the turret.'

There is not a shadow of a doubt that, despite Sacco's drinking habits and his way with women, on the site there could not have been an abler man in control. At last the time came when the painters left, the rubble was cleared from the site, the hall stood out on the grassy slope – a credit to Mr Harvey's efforts and a credit to Sacco and his men. Bert Harvey told Sacco he would be glad if he stayed on until the house was ready for occupation.

'Stay on, Sacco, sleep here if you like and keep an eye on the furniture as it arrives.'

'As you say, Sir,' Sacco replied as he pushed his pay packet into the top pocket of his overalls. 'I see you have a fine grand piano in the drawing-room. It's locked; what a pity!'

'You play the piano, Sacco?'

'Well, you may say I have an inkling how to produce some sort of music from the ivories.'

'Here's the key, boy. Just play when you feel like it in an evening, but keep it locked – it is valuable, you know.'

Then the landscape gardeners arrived, and being early autumn they slept in the billiard room – a sort of annex to the main hall. On Friday nights Mr Harvey was so looking forward to living in the hall and so pleased as usual with the finish of the work and the finished landscape gardens that he offered to take Sacco home to the harness room in the Rolls.

'If it's in order with you, Sir, we have a little party arranged tonight here with the gardeners. Becky will be cycling over with Milko, my good friend the dairyman. They will bring some food and drink from the Dragon.'

'What an excellent idea. I would love to stay but have a board meeting in Birmingham.' Reaching to the back seat of the Rolls, Bert Harvey produced two bottles of whisky. 'That will keep the cold out, Sacco. You have the key to the piano?'

Sacco, Milko, Becky and the gardeners ate and drank, but the whisky was discreetly hidden for later. 'Ramona, I'll Meet you by the Water Fall', they sang around the piano, the pianist's fingers gliding nimbly over the keys. About ten o'clock Milko and the girls cycled home, the midnight milkman to draw the milk from his Rubies and Becky to get back to Millie's.

By candlelight the gardeners drew the cork from the whisky. Sacco smacked his toothless gums as he drank from a tea cup. 'It's the classical music I love to hear,' one of Harvey's men said, 'but you have no music for that, Sacco?'

Then came that artful look from our Charlie Kunz as he said, 'I play by ear. Do you like Beethoven, Chopin or Mozart?' They all sang in unison 'The Miner's Dream of Home.' 'Very touching,' the head gardener said. The whisky reddened the faces of the candlelit company in Harvey's drawing-room as Sacco played the 'Lost Chord'.

'How often,' he said 'have I been seated at the organ when an old melody came as if from nowhere. We are weary, neighbours, but definitely not ill at ease. Now before I play "God Save the King", listen to this.' Sacco now started something different, with a religious flavour. Something that could go on to eternity. 'Jesu, Joy of Man's Desiring' rang through the great high-ceilinged drawing-room, through the open door into the panelled hall. Taffy Edwards, the local policeman, listened through the window, walked in through the unbarred door, stood with the rest and mingled his Welsh tenor voice to good effect with the company. 'Indeed that's a fine piece of music, Sacco. Could we sing "Myvanwy" like they do at Treorchy where I come from?'

'Anything to oblige, Taffy. It's late now but I finish here tonight and shall miss the old hall.'

'Never thought the Evesham Vale would ring with song like

the Welsh valleys, but Sacco, easy on the hard stuff, you have to cycle home.'

Sacco sat well back on his stool. In front of him were several hundred pounds worth of grand piano. 'Now, Taffy, not all for the Welsh tonight,' and tenderly he played 'All in an April Evening'. 'That's the Glasgow Orpheus Choir's special.' The men took Sacco's cue and sang 'The sheep with their little lambs' until they could just imagine the springtime with ewes and lambs being driven unwillingly along the crooked roads near the hall. 'When I came in,' Taffy remarked, 'I did enjoy the piece you played and sang.' So once again Sacco's fingers struck the ivory keys and began the repitition of 'Jesu, Joy of Man's Desiring'. Taffy wished them goodnight. The gardeners went instinctively to their lodgings. Sacco locked the hall and gave them the key, then put a full bottle of cider in his bag which he slung over the handlebars of his bike. Another bottle of cider he put in his coat pocket, and steered for the harness room. First a right-hand bend, then another right-hand bend, a left-hand one and an awkward angle between two houses, then the road widened. His cycle lamp picked out the curving glass verges of the road and Sacco was well on his way to the harness room and home.

Then it happened! The few bedroom lights of the village meant that most folk were in bed. Outside the Dragon, Wisdom Loveridge talked with Tat Steward. ''Night, Sacco,' Tat called after the bike had passed and Sacco turned round. The bag with the bottle of cider wedged between the front forks and the wheel, pitching Sacco into the road. He lay still, face downwards, the bike went into the roadside ditch. Tat's lantern showed signs of blood dripping from the mason's chin.

'This unt a job for the likes a we,' he said to Wisdom, ''tis a case for Dr Overthrow. He unt a bed, thur's a light of his candle in the surgery, he's mixing jallop or summat, I'll fetch him.' Meanwhile Milko was delivering his midnight milk. Flora lit a candle and she, Harbour Lights' widow, peeped from the same bedroom window as Tiddley.

'Look ya,' said Harry to Fred Cooper as they met by the

Dragon gate, 'look at Coney Burrows. No doubt they lies anant each other these cold nights.'

Dr Overthrow came, candle in jam jar, to the scene. Milko was singing 'We Plough the Fields and Scatter the Good Seed on the Land.'

'Shut that rattle,' Tat shouted, 'thur has been a hackciddent, let's have your lantern.'

The doctor looked at Sacco on the roadside. He saw in the light of Milko's lantern a stream of amber liquid running down the road from the mason's trousers. 'Don't move him,' he said. 'I suspect a burst bladder. It can happen from an injury by the handlebars.'

'Poor Sacco,' Flora said as she and Tiddley came half-clothed to the little group. 'That will mean hospital.'

The doctor with Milko's lantern looked closer at the injured man. The light attracted him and he, rolling over, sat up.

'Hold him,' the doctor said. 'Don't let him move.'

Sacco opened his eyes to the circle saying, 'If it isn't the good Dr Overthrow himself – and Tat and Wisdom. I did have a bottle of cider in my pocket, but alas it's broken and soaked my best trousers.'

'So that's the liquid running down the village street,' the doctor said with a chuckle. 'Sit him up, Tat, you and Wisdom help him into Milko's float. You will take him home to the harness room.'

Meanwhile Flora Lights had brought a basin of lukewarm water, some soap and a towel and was washing and towelling the blood-smeared face of Sacco. The villagers went home to their beds, the doctor to his surgery, while Milko drove his nag down the village street, Sacco sitting in the float on an upturned bucket. 'All is Safely Gathered in,' the midnight milkman sang as they approached the harness room. Sacco lit the oil lamp and poked the dying fire. 'In a hurry my good friend?' he said, putting a few lumps of coal in the grate.

'No, Milko's never in a hurry, not when there is an emergency like tonight.'

'I'm sorry, Milko, but I can't offer you a drink. Have you a little of the old lactic fluid in your churn?'

'Of course, it's still warm from the cows.'

From the shelf above the grate, Sacco reached unsteadily for two crock mugs. 'Tot out, Milko. A half a pint of your milk will do us both good.' Then putting the two mugs on his little deal table, Sacco, half-fuddled with whisky, half-stunned by his fall, whispered to Milko, 'Wait a minute, be seated opposite me, I'll say grace.' Milko pushed back his mop of blond hair and waited. 'It's one the Rev Vernon says at the bell ringers' supper!' They sat with eyes closed as Sacco recited:

> Benedictus, benedicat
> Rough my voice but I've a quire
> Fit to join the angel's lutes.
> Robins, thrushes, wrens aspire
> In the spring with blackbird's flutes
> Chiff chaff, finch and willow wren
> With my glad heart chants Amen.

'Amen,' said Milko.

'Just a thought, my friend, that I have been spared tonight. I might have broken my neck on the bike. Then thanks to the good doctor, to Flora Lights and most of all to my companion in this life, Arthur Gilson, whose float at midnight brought me home, here I am by my own fireside, the old football boots slung from the harness rack, sitting to commune with you over a mug of milk. Do you live in love and charity with your neighbours, Milko?'

'Can't say I've ever been in love, Sacco.'

'Then commune with me, not from the silver chalice at the church or the ink pot glasses of the chapel, commune with me with rich milk from the Rubies.'

Together they drank and refilled the mugs. Drank milk which should have been delivered to Cyril and Gunner. 'I see you have an organ now,' Milko said as he walked across the harness room with his lantern. 'A harmonium, to be precise, and a piano in the corner. *Nux* something it says on the stops,'

Milko observed. 'I wish that I could play.'

Sacco straightened his bow tie, looked at Milko, then putting his hand on his shoulder said, 'My good friend you have never lived.'

Milko looked downcast as he answered, 'Why?'

'Well, you see,' Sacco went on, 'first of all you say you have never been in love. It's true, you did couple with Amy on Jubilee night — that's what Vernon and Gunner would call satisfying the carnal desires. Then your only music is the sound of the cows' milk in the pail and your singing of harvest hymns into the night.'

'Play the organ, Sacco, let's sing tonight.'

Sacco looked into the fire which had brightened, casting shadows across the dimly lit room. Poking it with an old stair rod he said, 'My fingers have been gliding over the ivories of Mr Harvey's grand piano in a drawing-room like a marble hall. To play the harmonium after that would take the music of "Jesu, Joy of Man's Desiring" from my soul.'

'Play a piece from the chapel then,' Milko insisted. 'I was the Good Samaritan to you tonight.'

Sacco drew his chair to the harmonium, pedalled until the wind hummed through the instrument, then he pulled out the stops and his fingers struck a chord. 'I might manage a piece or two, but my old legs ache after the fall. Then yesterday I buried an old peapicker, he was but five foot and a tater and the undertaker put him in a box about six foot four. Remember Darkie? He has got room in his narrow bed tonight. 'I'll tell you a secret,' Sacco said. 'The chap from Evesham had undoubtedly got a coffin he wanted to get rid of, but it was me who dug the grave, moving all that unnecessary earth.'

Sacco's fingers played the first few lines of 'The Old Rugged Cross'. Milko sang 'On a Hill far away stood an old rugged cross, an emblem of suffering and shame.' Sacco, knowing the words by heart, led the milkman on until the chorus, 'So we'll cherish the old rugged cross, till my trophies at last I lay down. We'll cling to the old rugged cross and exchange it one day for a crown.'

Farmer Dunn, hearing the music, slipped his heavy coat over his night shirt and in leather slippers crept through the building where his governess cart stood long unused and paused by the harness room door. As Sacco went once again through the old hymn he was joined by his sister Kate in her scarlet dressing gown. Together they stood, not uttering a single word. Then Kate said, 'I wonder whether our kindly mason and the milkman will get their crown.'

Outside, looking at the stars and the moon rising over the Cotswolds, Farmer Dunn said, 'You know, Kate, on nights like this it's easy for a farmer to believe that somewhere up yonder some power sets the seasons. Sacco and Milko will get their crown.'